Pressure Enthalpy
Without Tears

Authored by: Eugene Silberstein, M.S., CMHE, BEAP/The HVAC Prof, Inc.

esco press

UNION CWA LABEL
PRINTING SECTION
CHICAGO, IL

Published by:
ESCO Press
PO Box 521
Mount Prospect Il 60056
Phone: 800-726-9696
Fax: 800-546-3726
Website: www.escogroup.org

ISBN 10: 090-07169-02
ISBN 13: 978-0-9907169-0-7

This book was written as a general guide. The author/s and publisher have neither liability nor can they be responsible to any person or entity for any misunderstanding, misuse, or misapplication that would cause loss or damage of any kind, including loss of rights, material, or personal injury, alleged to be caused directly or indirectly by the information contained in this book.

Printed in the United States of America
7 6 5 4 3 2 1

First Printing, January 2006
Second Printing, September 2007
Third Printing, September 2008
Fourth Printing, October 2009
Fifth Printing, August 2010
Sixth Printing, August, 2011
Seventh Printing, August, 2012
Eighth Printing, August, 2013

Dedicated to my dear friend Dan Holohan, for the gentle but firm nudging to get this project completed, and the Heating, Ventilation, Air Conditioning and Refrigeration students at Suffolk County Community College, Class of 2006.

About the Author

Eugene Silberstein, M.S., CMHE, BEAP

Over the past thirty plus years, Eugene has been involved in all aspects of the HVAC/R industry from field technician and system designer to company owner, teacher, administrator, consultant and author. Eugene is presently the lead faculty member for the HVAC/R program at Suffolk County Community College in Brentwood, New York. Eugene has twenty years of teaching experience and has taught at Apex Technical School and Nassau BOCES. Eugene is particularly excited about his present position as an Assistant Professor at Suffolk County Community College, as this is the only institution on Long Island to offer, not only a one-year certificate in HVAC/R, but also a two-year Associates of Applied Science degree, A.A.S., in HVAC/R.

Eugene earned his dual Bachelors Degree from The City College of New York and his Masters of Science degree from Stony Brook University, where he specialized in Energy and Environmental Systems, studying renewable and sustainable energy sources such as wind, solar, geothermal, biomass and hydropower. He earned his Certified Master HVAC/R Educator credential from HVAC Excellence and the ESCO Group after completing a battery of 7 educator-level examinations in a variety of content areas including Air Conditioning, Refrigeration, Heating, Heat Pumps and Electricity. Eugene also carries the BEAP credential issued by ASHRAE. This credential classifies Eugene as a Building Energy Assessment Professional.

As an active member of both ASHRAE and RSES, Eugene served as the subject matter expert and wrote the production scripts for over thirty education videos directly relating to our industry in addition to authoring the number one HVAC/R textbook in the industry, "*Refrigeration and Air Conditioning Technology, 7th Edition*" published by Cengage Learning. This book is used in over 1,000 schools both in this country and abroad to help individuals learn, and master, the skills required to service, install, design, service and troubleshoot HVAC/R equipment.

Other book credits include *Refrigeration and Air Conditioning Technology, 6th Edition, Residential Construction Academy: HVAC, 1st and 2nd Edition, Pressure Enthalpy Without Tears (2006), Heat Pumps (2002)* and, of course, *Psychrometrics Without Tears (2013)*. Eugene has also written a number of articles for industry newspapers and magazines.

Eugene was selected as one of the top three HVAC/R instructors in the country for the 2005/2006, 2006/2007 and 2007/2008 academic school years by the Air Conditioning and Refrigeration Institute (ARI), now AHRI, and the Air Conditioning, Heating and Refrigeration (ACHR) News.

About the Book

Over the years, much has been written on the subject of pressure-enthalpy. A good portion of this material has been geared toward the engineer for the sole purpose of system design. This book presents the concepts of pressure enthalpy in a manner that will appeal to the service technician in a way that encourages this valuable tool to be used as an aid in system troubleshooting, evaluation and the start up processes.

The technician's most useful tools have traditionally been a thermometer, gauge manifold and a keen eye. The thermometer provides vital information about the sensible heat transfers that take place in an air conditioning or refrigeration system. The gauge manifold, however, provides information about the latent heat transfers that are taking place in the system. Both of these tools provide integral pieces to the puzzle we call an air conditioning or refrigeration system. Separately, they have limited value. Used together, you have the basis for a sound, systematic troubleshooting technique.

There are some practical problems, however. To inspect the condensing unit, we need to head out to the back yard. To check the evaporator we need to climb into the attic or head down into the basement. Because of the very nature of the systems on which we work, it is impossible to get a complete picture of the system at a single glance. The pressure enthalpy chart enables us to do just that. With a completed pressure enthalpy plot, we can look at sensible and latent heat transfers, while looking at the compressor, condenser, metering device and evaporator… all at the same time.

Our book starts by reviewing the basic vapor-compression refrigeration cycle, as well as the concepts of superheat, subcooling and the pressure/temperature relationship. This provides a valuable review for the seasoned professional and also allows those new to the industry to hit the ground running with vital information.

The book then turns to pressure enthalpy, where the discussion begins with the basics of the chart itself, giving an overview of the meaning and purpose for every line on the chart. Simplified charts are used to enable the reader to gain a solid foundation of the concepts that we later build on.

The plotting of actual systems follows next. This involves plotting out units that are operating correctly so that we can see what properly operating systems look like on the chart. With practice, the process of plotting can take as little as two minutes.

With the completed plot in hand, we next turn to the evaluation of the system parameters that include net refrigeration effect, heat of work, heat of compression, mass flow rate per ton, theoretical horsepower per ton, total heat of rejection, mass flow rate of the system, evaporator capacity, condenser capacity, compressor capacity, coefficient of performance and energy efficiency ratio. These are dynamic tools that enable a technician to analyze and troubleshoot a system with speed and precision.

Once we have learned to plot systems on the pressure enthalpy chart, we then start looking at systems that are operating with malfunctions such as dirty air filters, refrigerant overcharge, refrigerant undercharge, etc.

It is here that the reader can appreciate the power of the pressure enthalpy chart and its usefulness to effectively and accurately start up, troubleshoot and evaluate air conditioning and refrigeration systems.

I truly hope that the material contained in this book proves as useful to you as it has to me.

Enjoy!

Eugene Silberstein, M.S., CMHE, BEAP

The HVAC Prof. Inc.
150 Farm Road East
Wading River, NY 11792
(917) 428-0044

You can e-mail Eugene Silberstein at eugene.silberstein@yahoo.com.

Pressure Enthalpy Without Tears

Table of Contents

SECTION I

The Basic Refrigeration Cycle... 1
- Repeating vs. non-repeating cycles.............................. 1
- A visual representation of the basic refrigeration cycle........... 3
- The four major refrigeration system components.................... 3
- Sensible and latent heat transfers............................... 11
- Saturation temperatures, pressures and the temperature/pressure chart............................. 13
- Pressure conversions.. 19
- Evaporator and system superheat................................. 23
- Condenser subcooling.. 29
- Putting it together... 34

SECTION II

The Pressure Enthalpy Chart... 37
- What do all of these lines mean? 37
- The basic refrigeration cycle and the pressure enthalpy chart 45
- System characteristics: Net Refrigeration Effect, NRE............. 51
- System characteristics: Mass Flow Rate per Ton................... 53
- System characteristics: Heat of Work, HOW....................... 55
- System characteristics: Compression Ratio....................... 57
- System characteristics: Heat of Compression, HOC................ 60
- System characteristics: Coefficient of Performance 62
- System characteristics: The Mysterious 42.42.................... 64
- System characteristics: Theoretical Horsepower per Ton.......... 66
- System characteristics: Total Heat of Rejection , THOR.......... 68
- System characteristics: Mass Flow Rate of the System............ 70
- System characteristics: Evaporator Capacity.................... 72
- System characteristics: Condenser Capacity..................... 74
- System characteristics: Compressor Capacity.................... 77
- System characteristics: Energy Efficiency Ratio, EER........... 78
- System characteristics: SEER................................... 80

SECTION III

Pressure Enthalpy: Plotting the System... 82
- System #1: Normal Operating Conditions (High temp)............ 82
- System #2: Normal Operating Conditions (Med temp)............ 94
- System #3: Medium Temp System with a defective
  evaporator fan motor (same system as system #2)................. 106
- System Comparison: System #2 vs. System #3..................... 110
  - Compression Ratio... 111
  - Net Refrigeration Effect, NRE................................ 112
  - Heat of Compression, HOC.................................... 112
  - Heat of Work, HOW... 112
  - Total Heat of Rejection, THOR............................... 113
  - Coefficient of Performance, COP............................. 113
  - Mass Flow Rate per Ton, MFR/ton............................. 113
  - Theoretical Horsepower per Ton, THp/ton..................... 114
  - Mass Flow Rate of the System, MFR/system................... 114
  - Capacity of the Evaporator................................... 115
  - Capacity of the Condenser................................... 115
  - Capacity of the Compressor.................................. 115
  - EER and SEER.. 116
- System #4: R-22 System Undercharge (A/C Application)......... 117
- System Comparison: System #1 vs. System #4..................... 121
- System #5: R-410A System (A/C Application, 40°F evaporator).. 122
- System Comparison: System #1 vs. System #5..................... 126
- System #6: R-410A System (A/C Application, 45°F evaporator).. 127
- System Comparison: System #5 vs. System #6..................... 131
- References and Contacts.. 132
- Blank Pressure Enthalpy Charts.................................. 133
  - R-22... 133
  - R-134a... 134
  - R-410A... 135
  - R-123.. 136
  - R-407C... 137
  - MP39 (R-401A).. 138
- Test Your Pressure Enthalpy Knowledge.......................... 139
- Test Your Pressure Enthalpy Knowledge (Answers)................ 140
- More Cool Stuff... 142
  - Possible causes for high subcooling.......................... 143
  - Possible causes for low subcooling.......................... 144
  - Possible causes for low evaporator superheat............... 145
  - Possible causes for high evaporator superheat.............. 147
  - Possible causes for high subcooling and low superheat.... 148
  - Possible causes for high subcooling and high superheat.... 149
  - Heat pump stuff... 150

THE BASIC REFRIGERATION CYCLE

Repeating versus Non-Repeating Cycles

Before we begin our discussion of pressure-enthalpy, system plotting and system parameter evaluation, a relatively brief, graphical review of the basic refrigeration cycle is in order. The review that follows will present the basic refrigeration cycle in a manner that will ease us into our discussion of pressure-enthalpy, so please do not skip over it. We will create a visual representation of the basic vapor-compression cycle which will transition very nicely into a completed pressure-enthalpy plot as we work through this book. The completed pressure-enthalpy plot will enable us to evaluate the system as a whole, while still being able to concentrate on specific system parameters where needed.

The first thing that needs to be addressed is the fact that the basic vapor-compression refrigeration cycle is a repeating cycle, Figure 1. A repeating cycle starts and ends at the same point. Simply stated, when the refrigerant has completed one complete path through the system, it returns to the same place it started from and is in the same exact condition as when it started. It should also be noted that, as the refrigerant circulates through the system, the refrigerant supply is not depleted. We can easily compare our repeating cycle to its opposite, a non-repeating cycle, by looking at a car engine. A non repeating cycle, Figure 2, starts and ends at different points.

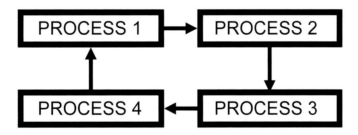

Figure 1. Graphical representation of a repeating cycle

Figure 2. Graphical representation of a non-repeating cycle

In order for a car engine to operate, we need to supply it with gasoline, or fuel. We drive to the gas station and fill our tanks with gas as evidenced by the movement of that little line on the gas gauge from "E" to "F". Sorry for over-simplifying this, but the overall concept is super-important. Now that we've filled our gas tanks, we're ready to drive. As we do so, fuel is ignited, the engine turns, the car moves and we create exhaust which is released to the atmosphere. This (non-repeating) cycle takes fuel and turns it into exhaust and, as a result, we are able to travel. Once the gas tank is empty, the engine will fail to operate until the fuel supply is replenished.

Now, consider the possibilities if we were able to capture the exhaust from the car and somehow turn these vapors back into usable gas. In such a case, the car could, theoretically, drive forever without the driver ever having to stop to refuel. This would be a great thing, unless of course you are the owner of a gas station or the CEO of a large oil company.

The basic refrigeration cycle, however, does just that. It's a repeating cycle that does not deplete the resources that provide the refrigeration effect. Of course I am leaving the electricity usage out of this discussion. No matter what point you start tracing out the refrigerant flow, when you return to that same point, the conditions will be exactly the same as when you started and the amount of refrigerant in the system will not change, provided, of course, that the system is leak-free.

The underlying concept of a repeating cycle is that whatever is done during one part of the cycle must later be un-done if we are to return to the same location and maintain the identical conditions. In the case of the basic air conditioning or refrigeration cycle, if the refrigerant pressure is increased at some point in the system, the pressure must later be decreased by the same amount to maintain the same pressure levels at the beginning and the end of the cycle. If heat is added to, or generated by, the system, this heat must later be rejected. If refrigerant undergoes a liquid-to-vapor transition in the system, the refrigerant must also undergo a vapor-to-liquid transition, and so on.

THE BASIC REFRIGERATION CYCLE

Visual Representation of the System and the Four Major System Components

Knowing now that the basic vapor-compression refrigeration cycle is a repeating cycle and that whatever is done in the system must, at some point in the future, be undone, our discussion will begin with a simple square, where each set of opposite sides represent the opposite transitions that the refrigerant undergoes as it flows through the system.

So as not to offend any other geometric shapes, as such is not my intention, the reason for selecting the square is simply because there are four major system components and four processes that take place during the course of the cycle. Two of these major components are responsible for pressure changes and the remaining two components are heat transfer surfaces and are responsible for the changes of state that the refrigerant undergoes. The four mini-processes that make up the basic refrigeration cycle are as follows:

- Increasing the pressure of the vapor refrigerant
- Decreasing the pressure of the liquid refrigerant
- Condensing vapor refrigerant into a liquid
- Evaporating liquid refrigerant into a vapor

Each of these mini-processes, each achieved by one of the four major system components, represents one side of the square.

Figure 3 shows our square. The top of the square represents high pressure and high temperature and, since the opposite sides represent opposite transitions and conditions, the bottom of the square will represent low pressure and low temperature. The pressure and temperature conditions are bundled together because of the pressure/temperature relationships that saturated refrigerants follow. More on this later.

Since each side of the square represents one of the processes just listed as well as one of the four main system components, it is important to visualize and understand that all interconnecting piping and other components in the active refrigerant circuit must be located at the corners of the square.

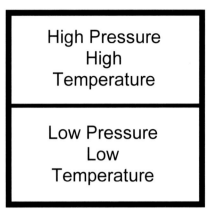

Figure 3. High pressure, high temperature refrigerant is present at the top of the square, while low pressure, low temperature refrigerant is present at the bottom.

The left side of the square will represent liquid refrigerant and the right side will represent vapor as in Figure 4.

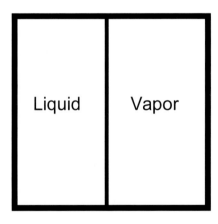

Figure 4. The left and right sides of the square represent liquid and vapor respectively.

By combining Figure 3 and Figure 4, we get the following, Figure 5, where H.P.H.T. represents high pressure, high temperature refrigerant and L.P.L.T. represents low pressure, low temperature refrigerant.

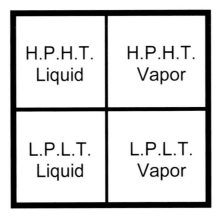

Figure 5. Combination of Figures 3 and 4 to divide the square into four quadrants.

To summarize the diagram thus far:

Top right corner   High Pressure, High Temperature Vapor
Top left corner   High Pressure, High Temperature Liquid
Bottom left corner   Low Pressure, Low Temperature Liquid
Bottom right corner   Low Pressure, Low Temperature Vapor

Now, we have to move around this square just as refrigerant will move through our system. We will use a counterclockwise path around the square as shown in Figure 6.

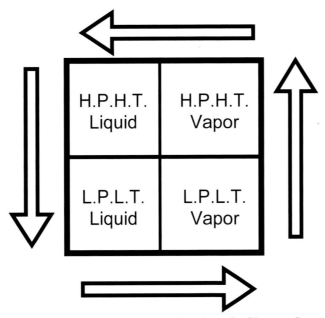

Figure 6. The arrows indicate the direction of refrigerant flow.

Now, we will begin the path around the square starting at the bottom right corner. From the bottom right corner, refrigerant vapor, as indicated by the information in the two right-hand boxes, travels up the right side of the square. Along this portion of the path the refrigerant changes from a low pressure, low temperature vapor to a high pressure, high temperature vapor, as in Figure 7. The laws of physics dictate that there is a definite relationship between the pressure, temperature and volume of fluids. Pressure and temperature have a direct relationship. If one (pressure or temperature) increases the other increases and if one decreases, the other decreases. Volume has an inverse relationship with pressure and temperature. If the volume is decreased, the temperature and pressure will increase. If the volume is increased, the temperature and pressure will decrease. Since the pressure and temperature are increasing as we follow the arrow up, the volume of the vapor refrigerant is getting smaller. This can be accomplished in a number of ways, but the most common method of reducing the volume of a vapor is to decrease the volume of the space that the vapor can occupy. Hence, the refrigerant is being compressed into a smaller and smaller space. The system component that accomplishes the compression process is referred to as the compressor.

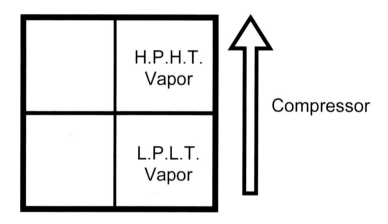

Figure 7. The pressure and temperature of the refrigerant are increased in the compressor.

Side Note:

> Compressors that physically reduce the available space for the refrigerant to occupy are referred to as positive displacement compressors. Common types of positive displacement compressors are the rotary, reciprocating, rotary screw and scroll compressor. The centrifugal compressor, which utilizes high speed fans and centrifugal force to push refrigerant into a smaller and smaller space, is referred to as a kinetic, not a positive, displacement compressor.

Now, at the top right corner of the square, the outlet of the compressor, the state of the refrigerant is that of a high temperature, high pressure vapor. From this point, the refrigerant moves from right to left across the top of the square and transitions to a high temperature, high pressure liquid, Figure 8. The pressure of the refrigerant remains the

6

same, although the temperature of the refrigerant does change. The changes in temperature will be addressed a little later on, but the important issue for our present discussion is that both the temperature and pressure of the refrigerant are high.

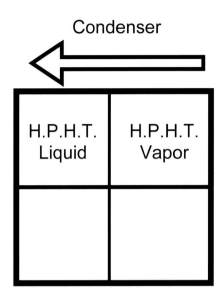

Figure 8. High pressure vapor condenses to a liquid in the condenser.

What is taking place across the top of the square is a change in state from vapor to liquid. The process where a vapor turns to a liquid is referred to as condensing and the system component represented by the top portion of the square is the condenser. In the order for the condensing process to take place, heat must be rejected from the refrigerant. If you've ever walked down the street past a window air conditioner and gotten a face full of hot air, you have experienced the condenser rejecting heat first hand. Well, if the condenser is rejecting heat from the system, there must be heat being added to the system at some other point. We'll get to that soon.

We now find ourselves at the top left corner and the state of the refrigerant is now a high pressure, high temperature liquid. On the right side of the square, we turned a low pressure, low temperature vapor into the high pressure, high temperature vapor. Since we must undo everything that was done in the cycle, the left side of the square must change high pressure, high temperature liquid into a low pressure, low temperature liquid, as shown in Figure 9.

The device that accomplishes this task is the metering device, also known as the expansion device. The device meters the correct amount of refrigerant into the next system component, the evaporator, and facilitates the expansion of the refrigerant once it gets there. This is accomplished, in its simplest terms, by creating a restriction to flow, just as a car accident that blocks a lane or two on the Interstate does, Figure 10.

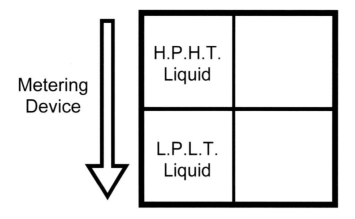

Figure 9. The metering device reduces the temperature and pressure of the refrigerant.

The car accident creates a restriction that forces all of the cars into a single lane, in effect reducing this highway to a one-lane road. As you can see in the figure, the traffic is backing up before the accident as the motorists wait to pass the accident or point of restriction. Once past the accident, the vehicles can resume their normal pace.

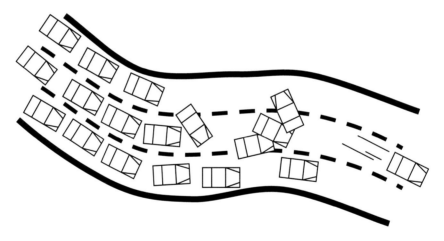

Figure 10. A pressure drop is created across a restriction.

Although this example may be over-simplified, we have "high pressure" before the metering device, just as we have backed up cars before the accident, and "low pressure" after the metering device, just as we have free traffic flow after the accident.

At this point, the refrigerant is a low pressure, low temperature liquid as it begins to move across the bottom of the square from left to right. The bottom of the square represents a change from the low pressure, low temperature liquid to a low pressure, low temperature vapor, Figure 11. The pressure and temperature of the refrigerant remains constant (for the most part, but we'll get to that in a little while), but the refrigerant is undergoing a liquid-to-vapor change of state. When a liquid turns to a vapor, the liquid evaporates and the component that facilitates this process is called the evaporator.

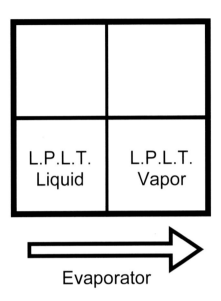

Figure 11. Liquid refrigerant vaporizes in the evaporator.

Just as a vessel of water produces steam when heated, Figure 12, the refrigerant must absorb heat in order to evaporate. In both cases, the liquid is absorbing heat and changing state from a liquid to a vapor.

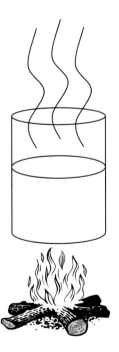

Figure 12. Liquids vaporize with the addition of heat.

At the conclusion of this last step, the refrigerant, a low pressure, low temperature vapor, is back at the lower right-hand corner and ready to begin another cycle. The complete cycle is shown in Figure 13.

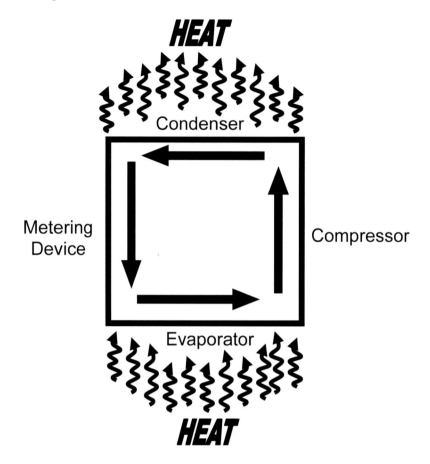

Figure 13. The basic vapor-compression refrigeration cycle.

THE BASIC REFRIGERATION CYCLE

Sensible and Latent Heat Transfers

Having covered the basic refrigeration cycle in its simplest terms, we will now take the next step by incorporating other concepts and terminology to complete the picture and increase our understanding of the refrigeration cycle. The purpose of air conditioning and refrigeration equipment is, in a nutshell, to transfer heat from one place to another. Heat transfer takes place naturally when a warmer substance comes in contact with a cooler substance and the direction of this heat transfer is from the warmer substance to the cooler one. This heat transfer will continue until both substances are at the same temperature. For example, consider the two beakers of water in Figure 14. Both beakers contain 1 pound of water. The water in the left beaker is at a temperature of 70°F, while the temperature of the water in the right beaker is 60°F.

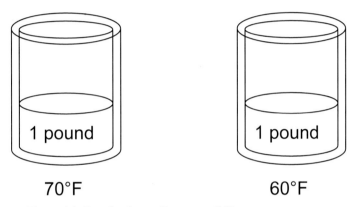

Figure 14. Two beakers of water at different temperatures.

If the contents of the left beaker was poured into the right beaker, the 70-degree water would transfer heat to the 60-degree water until a final temperature of 65 degrees was reached, Figure 15. The 65°F temperature is the midpoint between the two initial temperatures and, since the quantities of water in this example are the same, the final temperature will be midway between the two initial temperatures.

Figure 15. Resulting mixed water temperature is between the
temperatures of the individual samples.

Now let's consider the temperature of the air surrounding this beaker. If the surrounding air temperature is lower than 65°F, the water in the beaker will transfer heat to the surrounding air and the temperature of the water will drop. If the surrounding air temperature is higher than 65°F, the surrounding air will transfer heat to the water in the beaker and the temperature of the water will rise.

The above examples illustrated heat transfer and how we were able to establish heat transfers were taking place by the changes in the temperatures of the air and water. When we are able to measure changes in temperatures of a substance, a sensible heat transfer has taken place. *Sensible heat transfers are characterized by the fact that we can easily measure these changes with thermometers.* For example, changing the temperature of a piece of steel from 80°F to 100°F is an example of a sensible heat transfer.

Another type of heat transfer is called a latent heat transfer. *Latent heat transfers are often referred to as "hidden" heat transfers, as they cannot be measured with a thermometer.* Consider a one-pound block of ice that we want to melt. The initial temperature of the ice is 32°F and the temperature of the resulting water immediately after the ice has melted is also 32°F. How did the ice melt? Well, we had to add heat to the ice to melt it, but the temperature of the ice/water did not change. Where did the heat go?

The heat that was added to the ice was absorbed by the ice and was used to change the state of the ice to water while keeping the temperature constant. *Latent heat transfers, therefore result in a change of state with no change in temperature.*

A very common example of a latent heat transfer is the heating of water on the stove. Once the water is heated to 212°F it begins to boil and change state from a liquid to a vapor. This change of state occurs at 212°F (at atmospheric conditions) and adding additional heat will not raise the temperature of the water above 212°F, but will cause more of the water to vaporize.

Side note:

> It should be noted that much more heat is transferred during latent heat transfers than during sensible heat transfers. For example, it takes one btu of heat energy to raise the temperature of one pound of water one degree Fahrenheit, but 144 btu to change one pound of ice at 32°F to one pound of water at 32°F and 970 btu to change one pound of water at 212°F to one pound of steam at 212°F.

We will delve deeper into the sensible and latent heat transfer issues a little later when we put the entire system together.

THE BASIC REFRIGERATION CYCLE

Saturation Temperatures, Pressures and the Pressure/Temperature Chart

In an air conditioning or refrigeration system, refrigerant can be present in any one of three different states. These are:

- 100% Liquid
- 100% Vapor
- Mixture of liquid and vapor

Referring back to our basic refrigeration cycle, Figure 16, we can now begin to evaluate the state and condition of the refrigerant at any given point, as well as the type of heat transfer that is taking place at any point in the system. From the right-hand side of the figure we can see that there is vapor at both the inlet and the outlet of the compressor. Since there is (ideally) only vapor in the compressor, it can be argued that a sensible heat transfer is taking place in the compressor. If there was a change of state either from liquid to vapor or vapor to liquid, there would have been a latent heat transfer.

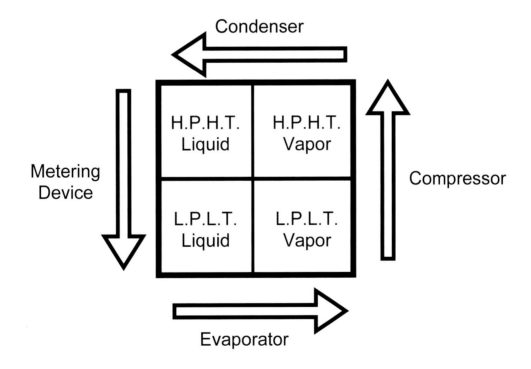

Figure 16. The basic refrigeration cycle.

The condenser and the evaporator, on the other hand, facilitate a change of state. The condenser, which is responsible for rejecting system heat, causes refrigerant to condense from a vapor to a liquid. In practice, the refrigerant enters the condenser as 100% vapor and leaves as 100% liquid. During the condensing process, the refrigerant is part liquid and part vapor, so the refrigerant is present in all three states mentioned above.

When refrigerant is a mixture of liquid and vapor, the refrigerant is said to be saturated. Any heat added to or removed from the refrigerant while it is saturated will result in no temperature change. The exception to this is when the refrigerant is either a completely saturated liquid or vapor.

Consider the example of a refrigerant that is presently a 50% vapor-liquid mix. Adding heat to the refrigerant will cause more of the liquid to vaporize causing the percentage of vapor in the mixture to increase and the percentage of liquid to decrease, Figure 17. Similarly, removing heat from the 50% vapor/liquid mixture will cause more of the vapor to condense into a liquid, increasing the percentage of liquid refrigerant and decreasing the percentage of vapor in the mixture. During this process, the temperature of the refrigerant remains the same, as only a latent heat transfer is taking place.

Figure 17. Adding heat to a saturated refrigerant changes the state, not the temperature of the refrigerant.

Once the refrigerant leaves the condenser as a high pressure, high temperature liquid it enters the metering device. The refrigerant leaves the metering device as a saturated liquid that is at a lower temperature and pressure. A portion of the liquid vaporizes as it flows through and exits the metering device on its way into the evaporator. So, as far as the metering device is concerned, refrigerant enters as 100% liquid and leaves as a saturated mixture of liquid (approximately 80%) and vapor (approximately 20%).

Side note:

> The refrigerant that boils off into a vapor as it exits the metering device and enters the evaporator is referred to as flash gas. This term is used because, as liquid refrigerant leaves the metering device, it is exposed to an increase in volume (the evaporator) and immediately experiences a decrease in pressure. This decrease in pressure causes a portion of the liquid refrigerant to immediately flash off into a vapor. The good thing about flash gas is that, when the liquid flashes into a vapor, or evaporates, it absorbs heat from the surrounding liquid refrigerant, lowering the temperature of the refrigerant in the evaporator. The bad news is that too much flash gas reduces the amount of latent heat transfer that takes place in the evaporator, lowering the efficiency of the system.

In the evaporator, refrigerant undergoes a change of state from a saturated liquid to a vapor. The heat transfer that takes place in the evaporator is a latent heat transfer until all of the liquid refrigerant has vaporized. Once the refrigerant has become 100% vapor, any additional heat transfers in the evaporator are of the sensible type, Figure 18.

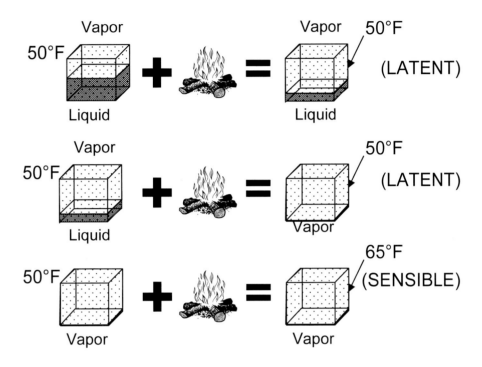

Figure 18. Examples of latent and sensible heat transfers.

As discussed in the previous paragraphs, a refrigerant is said to be saturated when a sample of the refrigerant contains both liquid and vapor. The percentages of liquid and vapor in the mixture are not important at this point, just the fact that there is a combination of both. For example, a 90% liquid – 10% vapor mixture of refrigerant is considered to be saturated, just as a 50% liquid – 50% vapor mixture is. The same argument can be made for a refrigerant mixture that contains 99.999% liquid and 0.001% vapor. For all intents and purposes, this refrigerant mixture is 100% liquid, but is still saturated and is referred to as a saturated liquid. Conversely, a refrigerant mixture that contains 99.999% vapor and 0.001% liquid is basically 100% vapor and is referred to as a saturated vapor.

The one property of saturated refrigerants that makes the job of the air conditioning and refrigeration technician easier is the fact that saturated refrigerants behave in a very predictable manner. Saturated refrigerants follow a pressure/temperature relationship that enables us to determine the temperature of a saturated refrigerant if the pressure of that saturated refrigerant is known. Similarly, if the temperature of a saturated refrigerant is known, we can easily determine the pressure of that refrigerant sample. This information is contained on the temperature/pressure chart, Figure 19.

TEMP °F	R-12	R-22	R-134a	R-410A
-60	19.0	12.0	--	0.3
-55	17.3	9.2	--	2.6
-50	15.4	6.2	--	5.0
-45	13.3	2.7	--	7.8
-40	11.0	0.5	14.7	9.8
-35	8.4	2.6	12.4	14.2
-30	5.5	4.9	9.7	17.9
-25	2.3	7.4	6.8	21.9
-20	0.6	10.1	3.6	26.4
-18	1.3	11.3	2.2	28.2
-16	2.0	12.5	0.7	30.2
-14	2.8	13.8	0.3	32.2
-12	3.6	15.1	1.2	34.3
-10	4.5	16.5	2.0	36.4
-8	5.4	17.9	2.8	38.7
-6	6.3	19.3	3.7	40.9
-4	7.2	20.8	4.6	42.3
-2	8.2	22.4	5.5	45.8
0	9.2	24.0	6.5	48.3
2	10.2	25.6	7.5	50.9
4	11.2	27.3	8.6	53.6
6	12.3	29.1	9.7	56.4
8	13.5	30.9	10.8	59.3
10	14.6	32.8	11.9	62.2
11	15.2	33.7	12.5	63.7
12	15.8	34.7	13.2	65.3
13	16.4	35.7	13.8	66.8
14	17.1	36.7	14.4	68.4

TEMP °F	R-12	R-22	R-134a	R-410A
15	17.7	37.7	15.1	70.0
16	18.4	38.7	15.7	71.6
17	19.0	39.8	16.4	73.2
18	19.7	40.8	17.1	75.0
19	20.4	41.9	17.7	76.7
20	21.0	43.0	18.4	78.4
21	21.7	44.1	19.2	80.1
22	22.4	45.3	19.9	81.9
23	23.4	46.4	20.6	83.7
24	23.9	47.6	21.4	85.5
25	24.6	48.8	22.0	87.3
26	25.4	49.9	22.9	90.2
27	26.1	51.2	23.7	91.1
28	26.9	52.4	24.5	93.0
29	27.7	53.6	25.3	95.0
30	28.4	54.9	26.1	97.0
31	29.2	56.2	26.9	99.0
32	30.1	57.5	27.8	101.0
33	30.9	58.8	28.7	103.1
34	31.7	60.1	29.5	105.1
35	32.6	61.5	30.4	107.3
36	33.4	62.8	31.3	108.4
37	34.3	64.2	32.2	111.6
38	35.2	65.6	33.2	113.8
39	36.1	67.1	34.1	116.0
40	37.0	68.5	35.1	118.3
41	37.9	70.0	36.0	120.5
42	38.8	71.4	37.0	122.9

TEMP °F	R-12	R-22	R-134a	R-410A
43	39.8	73.0	38.0	125.2
44	40.7	74.5	39.0	127.6
45	41.7	76.0	40.1	130.0
46	42.6	77.6	41.1	132.4
47	43.6	79.2	42.2	134.9
48	44.6	80.8	43.3	136.4
49	45.7	82.4	44.4	139.9
50	46.7	84.0	45.5	142.5
55	52.0	92.6	51.3	156.0
60	57.7	101.6	57.3	170.0
65	63.8	111.2	64.1	185.0
70	70.2	121.4	71.2	200.8
75	77.0	132.2	78.7	217.6
80	84.2	143.6	86.8	235.4
85	91.8	155.7	95.3	254.2
90	99.8	168.4	104.4	274.1
95	108.2	181.8	114.0	295.0
100	117.2	195.9	124.2	317.1
105	126.6	210.8	135.0	340.3
110	136.4	226.4	146.4	364.8
115	146.8	242.7	158.5	390.5
120	157.6	259.9	171.2	417.4
125	169.1	277.9	184.6	445.8
130	181.0	296.8	198.7	475.4
135	193.5	316.6	213.5	506.5
140	206.6	337.2	229.1	539.1
145	220.3	358.9	245.5	573.2
150	234.6	381.5	262.7	608.9

Figure 19. Temperature-pressure chart for R-12, R-22, R-134a and R-410A.

16

The left column contains the temperature scale in degrees Fahrenheit and ranges from -60°F to +150°F. The body of the chart contains the corresponding saturation pressures for four refrigerants: R-12, R-22, R-134a and R-410A. The italicized numbers in the body of the chart represent pressures below atmospheric (vacuum) in inches of Mercury.

Side note:

> It should be noted that there is a difference between a pressure/temperature chart and a temperature/pressure chart. On a t/p chart, as in Figure 19, the temperatures are listed on the left side of the chart, while the body of the chart contains the pressures for the listed refrigerants. On a p/t chart, the left side of the chart contains the saturation pressures, while the body of the chart contains the corresponding saturation temperatures.

The temperatures and pressures listed in the temperature/pressure chart, as mentioned before, are for saturated refrigerants only and provide the temperatures and pressures at which a change of state is taking place.

Example #1

> Consider an R-22 air conditioning system that has a low side pressure of 68.5 psig. At what temperature is the refrigerant undergoing a liquid-to-vapor change of state. In other words, what is the boiling temperature of the refrigerant?

Solution:

> We are looking for the boiling temperature of the refrigerant, which means we want the saturation temperature for that refrigerant at a pressure of 68.5 psig. In the main body of our temperature/pressure chart (the pressures) we locate 68.5 under R-22. Once this is located we move over to the left and read the saturation temperature of that refrigerant at the given pressure. In this case, the saturation temperature is 40°F, Figure 20. At 68.5 psig, R-22 boils at 40°F.

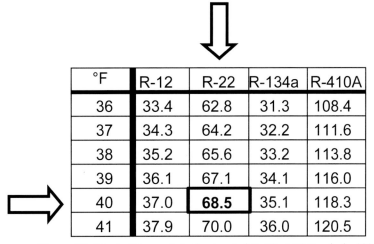

°F	R-12	R-22	R-134a	R-410A
36	33.4	62.8	31.3	108.4
37	34.3	64.2	32.2	111.6
38	35.2	65.6	33.2	113.8
39	36.1	67.1	34.1	116.0
40	37.0	**68.5**	35.1	118.3
41	37.9	70.0	36.0	120.5

Figure 20. The boiling point of saturated R-22 at 68.5 psig is 40°F.

Example #2

We have a medium temperature refrigeration system that operates with R-134a as its refrigerant. The evaporator saturation temperature is 25°F. What is the low side pressure of this system?

Solution:

In this case, we are given the evaporator saturation temperature and would like to determine the evaporator saturation pressure. This time, we look in the left-hand column to locate the saturation temperature of 25 degrees. Once this temperature has been located, we move to the right until we are in the R-134a column. The value in this box is the saturation pressure, which, in this case, is 22 psig.

In an air conditioning or refrigeration system, there are two system pressures: the high side pressure and the low side pressure. The high side pressure can be read at any available service port between the compressor discharge and the inlet of the metering device. Neglecting all pressure drops in the system, the high side pressure reading will be the same when taken at any high side service port. The temperature of the refrigerant at the various points will be different.

For example, a pressure reading at the outlet of the compressor may be, for an R-22 air conditioning system, 226.4 psig. This does not mean that the temperature of the refrigerant at this point is 110°F (from the t/p chart). What this reading provides is the saturation pressure, which corresponds to the temperature at which a vapor-to-liquid change of state will occur (condensing) on the high side of the system.

Remember that the compressor contains 100% vapor at its inlet and 100% vapor at its outlet. Therefore, refrigerant in the compressor does not follow a pressure/temperature relationship.

The low side system pressure can be read at any low side service port between the outlet of the metering device and the inlet of the compressor. As in the case of the high side pressure readings, this pressure reading will be the same no matter where the reading has been taken. The temperature of the refrigerant at these points will be different.

Consider a refrigeration system that has a low side pressure reading at the inlet of the compressor of 24.6 psig (R-12). The temperature of the refrigerant at that point will, ideally, not be 25°F (from the t/p chart). This is because the refrigerant at the inlet of the compressor is not saturated and does not follow a pressure/temperature relationship. The temperature of the refrigerant at the inlet of the compressor will be at some temperature higher than 25°F.

So, to sum up, when a latent heat transfer is taking place, the refrigerant follows a pressure/temperature relationship.

THE BASIC REFRIGERATION CYCLE

Pressure Conversions

When we begin our discussion of the pressure enthalpy chart, we will need to use absolute pressures instead of the gauge pressures that are found on the temperature/pressure chart and our gauge manifolds. The pressures that we read on our gauge manifolds negate the effects of atmospheric presusre, while absolute pressures do not. For example, if we disconnect a service hose from our gauge manifold, the gauge needle should point to 0 psig. This is the gauge reading and does not factor in the weight of the atmosphere above the gauge, which is about 15 pound per square inch at sea level. An absolute pressure reading at sea level will, therefore, be about 15 pounds per square inch. The actual pressure difference between absolute and gauge pressure (at sea level) is 14.696, which we round off to 15.

The pressure enthalpy chart requires that we use absolute, not gauge pressures. Because of this, we will need to know how to convert gauge pressures into an equivalent absolute pressure. Here is the information required to make such conversions.

Abbreviations:

　　　psig = Pounds per square inch gauge

　　　psia = Pounds per square inch absolute

Converting Gauge Pressures to Absolute Pressures
(For gauge pressures above or equal to 0 psig)

Add 15 to the gauge reading to obtain the pressure reading in psia

Example #3:

　　　Convert 0 psig to a psia reading

Solution:

　　　0 psig + 15 = 15 psia

Example #4:

　　　Convert 60 psig to a psia reading

Solution:

　　　60 psig + 15 = 75 psia

Converting Gauge Pressures to Absolute Pressures
(For gauge pressures below 0 psig)

Use the following formula to make the conversion:

$$psia = (30"Hg - Vacuum\ reading) \div 2$$

Example #5:

Convert a vacuum reading of 14"Hg to psia

Solution:

$psia = (30"Hg - Vacuum\ reading) \div 2$

$psia = (30"Hg - 14"Hg) \div 2$

$psia = 16 \div 2 = 8$

$14"Hg = 8\ psia$

Example #6:

Convert a vacuum reading of 30"Hg to psia

Solution:

$psia = (30"Hg - Vacuum\ reading) \div 2$

$psia = (30"Hg - 30"Hg) \div 2$

$psia = 0 \div 2 = 0$

$30"Hg = 0\ psia$

A reading of 0 psia represents a perfect vacuum

Converting Absolute Pressures to Gauge Pressures
(For absolute pressures above or equal to 15 psia)

Subtract 15 from the absolute pressure reading to obtain the pressure reading in psig.

Example #7:

Convert 80 psia to a psig reading

Solution:

80 psia - 15 = 65 psig

Example #8:

Convert 15 psia to a psig reading

Solution:

15 psia - 15 = 0 psig

Converting Absolute Pressures to Gauge Pressures
(For absolute pressures below 15 psia)
(Vacuum Region)

For absolute pressures below 15 psia, use the following formula:

Vacuum reading in "Hg = 30"Hg – 2(psia)

Example #9:

Convert 5 psia to a Vacuum reading in "Hg

Solution:

Vacuum reading in "Hg = 30"Hg – 2(psia)

Vacuum reading in "Hg = 30"Hg – 2(5 psia)

Vacuum reading in "Hg = 30"Hg – 10"Hg

Vacuum reading in "Hg = 20"Hg

5 psia = 20"Hg

Example #10:

Convert 10 psia to a Vacuum reading in "Hg

Solution:

Vacuum reading in "Hg = 30"Hg – 2(psia)

Vacuum reading in "Hg = 30"Hg – 2(10 psia)

Vacuum reading in "Hg = 30"Hg – 20"Hg

Vacuum reading in "Hg = 10"Hg

10 psia = 10"Hg

A conversion chart between "Hg and psia is provided in Figure 21.

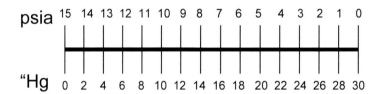

Figure 21. Pressure conversions from psia to inches of Mercury (vacuum).

THE BASIC REFRIGERATION CYCLE

Evaporator and System Superheat

Let's start this discussion with an air conditioning evaporator that is operating with a low side pressure of 68.5 psig. The temperature of the air in the occupied space is 70°F and the temperature of the air being supplied to the space is 50°F, Figure 22.

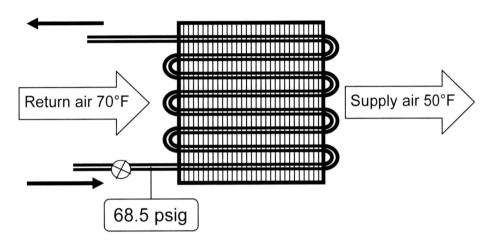

Figure 22. An R-22 evaporator operating at a pressure of 68.5 psig.

We can determine from the temperature/pressure chart that the liquid refrigerant is boiling off into a vapor at a temperature of 40°F, since we know that the low side pressure is 68.5 psig. The refrigerant enters the evaporator as a saturated refrigerant and is approximately 80% liquid and 20% vapor. As the refrigerant flows through the evaporator coil, heat from the 70°F return air is transferred to the saturated refrigerant. This causes more of the liquid to boil off into a vapor and the percentage of liquid decreases, while the percentage of vapor increases. During this latent heat transfer, the temperature of the refrigerant remains constant at 40°F. This latent heat transfer will continue until the last drop of liquid vaporizes.

Once all of the liquid has boiled off into a vapor, we are left with 100% vapor at a temperature of 40°F. Since the refrigerant is now no longer saturated, the temperature/pressure relationship no longer holds. As return air continues to pass over the evaporator coil the 70-degree air gives up heat to the 40-degree vapor refrigerant. Now, what happens to the heat that the refrigerant absorbs?

Since the refrigerant can no longer vaporize, as there is no more liquid, the absorbed heat is used to increase the temperature of the vapor. This heat transfer is no longer a latent heat transfer as the temperature of the vapor is increasing. The pressure of the refrigerant on the low side of the system, however, remains constant, Figure 23.

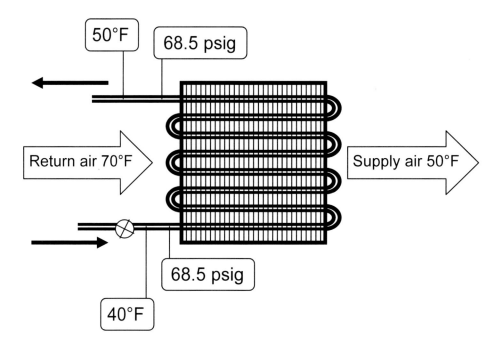

Figure 23. The pressure in the evaporator is the same at the inlet and the outlet, but the temperature of the refrigerant at the outlet of the coil is higher.

So, there are two types of heat transfer that are taking place in the evaporator. First, there is a latent heat transfer that takes place from the point the refrigerant leaves the metering device up to the point in the evaporator coil where the last drop of liquid can be found. Once again, during this heat transfer the temperature of the refrigerant remains constant but the liquid/vapor percentage change until there is only 100 percent vapor in the evaporator coil. Once the point is reached where there is no longer any liquid in the coil, the warmer air that is passing over the coil causes the temperature of the refrigerant vapor to increase, Figure 24. This is our sensible heat transfer and is called superheat.

Evaporator superheat is defined as the amount of sensible heat that is picked up in the evaporator coil after all of the liquid has vaporized.

The amount of evaporator superheat is determined partly by the point at which the last drop of liquid refrigerant can be found. If the last droplet of liquid is located close to the outlet of the evaporator coil, the amount of evaporator superheat will be low. If the refrigerant boils off quickly in the evaporator, the amount of evaporator superheat will be high.

Evaporator superheat can be calculated by subtracting the evaporator saturation temperature from the evaporator outlet temperature:

Evaporator Outlet Temperature

- Evaporator Saturation Temperature

Evaporator Superheat

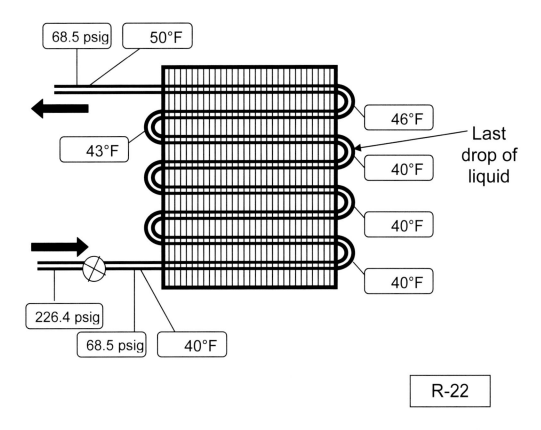

Figure 24. The last drop of liquid represents the point where the latent heat transfer ends and the sensible heat transfer (superheat) begins.

Example #11

Consider the evaporator shown in Figure 24. The evaporator saturation temperature is 40°F and the evaporator outlet temperature is 50°F.

Solution:

The evaporator superheat is, therefore, 50°F - 40°F = 10°F.

Example #12

We have an air conditioning system that is operating with R-410A as its refrigerant and the low side pressure of the system is 130 psig. The temperature reading at the outlet of the evaporator coil is 53°F. Calculate the evaporator superheat.

Solution:

Evaporator superheat is the difference between the evaporator outlet temperature and the evaporator saturation temperature. We are given the evaporator outlet temperature (53°F) and we need to find the evaporator saturation temperature. Since we are given the evaporator saturation pressure, we can use the temperature/pressure chart to determine the saturation temperature. We look up R-410A at 130 psig on the temperature/pressure chart to obtain a saturation temperature of 45°F. The superheat calculation is as follows:

Evaporator Superheat = Evaporator Outlet Temp – Evaporator Saturation Temp
Evaporator Superheat = 53°F – 45°F
Evaporator Superheat = 8°F

Example #13

Calculate the superheat of an R-12 evaporator that has a saturation pressure of 24.6 psig and an outlet temperature of 25°F.

Solution:

From the temperature/pressure chart, we can convert the saturation pressure of 24.6 psig to the saturation temperature of 25°F.

Evaporator Superheat = Evaporator Outlet Temp – Evaporator Saturation Temp
Evaporator Superheat = 25°F – 25°F
Evaporator Superheat = 0°F

Zero degrees of evaporator superheat indicates that the evaporator has saturated refrigerant at the outlet of the coil. This can be detrimental to the compressor as the pump is designed to handle vapor, not liquid.

Side note:

Normal evaporator superheat typically ranges from 8 to 12 degrees, but remember that each and every system is different and has different system requirements and design operating conditions.

When teaching those relatively new to the industry, it is always easier to relate relatively complex and confusing concepts in a manner that is completely unrelated to the material at hand to allow the learners to grasp the concepts. For those that are new to the industry and to those that are responsible for training those new to the industry, I offer the following to aid in the understanding of the concept just discussed.

Consider that you are lying on the beach of a deserted island. You look out over the ocean and all you see is the horizon in the distance. Above the horizon you see nothing but the blue air and below the horizon line, you see the water. At the horizon line, you see both the water and the air above it. All of a sudden, in a distance, you see a superhero fly through the air, Figure 25. You ask yourself the following question, "How high above the water is that superhero flying?"

This scene is not difficult to visualize and it can help clear up a lot of confusion. Here is the analysis:

- The superheating process takes place on the vapor side of the system, just as our superhero flies in air (vapor).
- Superheat calculations use the evaporator outlet temperature which is higher than the saturation temperature, just as the altitude of our flying superhero is higher than saturation (the horizon)
- *Super*-heat → *Super*-hero
- In order to determine how high our superhero is flying, we need to determine the distance between the hero and the water/air (saturation) line, just as we calculate evaporator superheat by determining the difference between the evaporator outlet temperature and the evaporator saturation temperature.
- Our superhero represents the outlet of the evaporator

Figure 25. Superheat analogy.

Having covered the concept of evaporator superheat, the last item in this section is system superheat. Since evaporator superheat is defined as the amount of superheat present in the evaporator, system superheat is the amount of superheat found in the system.

The superheating process begins when the last drop of liquid refrigerant in the evaporator vaporizes and continues until refrigerant vapor is discharged from the compressor. System superheat can, therefore, be defined by the following formula:

$$\frac{\text{Compressor Outlet Temperature} - \text{Evaporator Saturation Temperature}}{\text{System Superheat}}$$

Side note:

> Depending on the application and who you are talking to, system superheat can also be used to describe the amount of sensible heat picked up between the point where the last drop of liquid vaporizes and the point where the vapor *enters* the compressor.

THE BASIC REFRIGERATION CYCLE

Condenser Subcooling

The condenser is the heat exchange surface that is responsible for rejecting the system heat that is absorbed by the evaporator as well as additional heat picked up in the associated piping. In addition, the condenser rejects the heat that is concentrated in, and generated by the process of compression.

Three processes take place in the condenser, two of which are sensible heat transfers and the other is a latent heat transfer. These three processes are

- Desuperheating (a sensible heat transfer)
- Condensing (a latent heat transfer)
- Subcooling (a sensible heat transfer)

In our discussion of superheat, we established a number of things that are important to our discussion of subcooling. They are:

- Refrigerant picks up superheat from the point where the last drop of liquid is present in the evaporator to the point where the vapor refrigerant leaves the compressor.
- Refrigerant in the compressor is superheated and does not follow a temperature/pressure relationship.

With this in mind, we can establish that, since the refrigerant *in* the compressor is superheated and does not follow a temperature/pressure relationship, the refrigerant at the *outlet* of the compressor is a superheated vapor and does not follow a temperature either.

Since the refrigerant at the outlet of the compressor is superheated, it is at a temperature that is higher than the saturation temperature on the high side of the system. So, in order for the refrigerant to undergo the vapor-to-liquid state change, the refrigerant must first be cooled down to the saturation temperature. This process is referred to as desuperheating as the refrigerant must give up superheat in order to condense.

For example, consider an R-22 air conditioning system that is operating with a high side pressure of 226 psig and a compressor discharge temperature of 200°F. Let us also assume that the outside ambient temperature is about 80°F. From the temperature/pressure chart, we can see that the condenser saturation temperature that corresponds to the 226 psig high side pressure is 110°F. Now, in order for the refrigerant to condense into a liquid, the discharge vapor must be cooled from 200°F to 110°F. Since the outside ambient temperature (80°F) is lower than the 200°F compressor discharge vapor, a sensible heat transfer takes place and the temperature of the gas drops. This sensible heat transfer (desuperheating) continues until the temperature of the refrigerant drops to the condenser saturation temperature. Once the desuperheated vapor is cooled down to the saturation temperature, any additional heat loss by the refrigerant to the surrounding air will initiate the condensing (vapor-to-liquid) process, Figure 26.

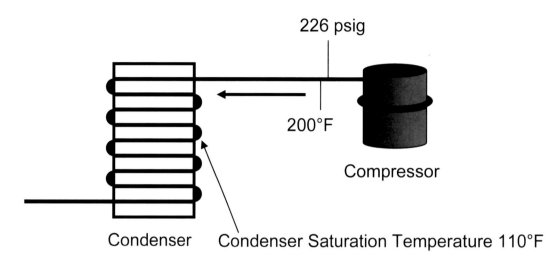

Figure 26. Hot gas from the compressor must give up sensible heat (superheat) before it can condense.

Once the refrigerant has desuperheated to the condenser saturation temperature and the condensing process has begun, the temperature of the refrigerant will remain constant, but the vapor/liquid percentages will change. Immediately after the desuperheating process has completed, the refrigerant will be 100% vapor and 0% liquid. As the change of state continues, the percentage of liquid in the mixture will increase and the percentage of vapor will decrease.

The condensing process, the second process that takes place in the condenser, takes place as the 110-degree refrigerant transfers heat to the 80-degree air that is passing over the condenser coil. This latent heat transfer will continue until the refrigerant is 100% liquid at a temperature of 110°F.

Once the refrigerant has completely condensed, the 110°F liquid will continue to give up heat to the 80-degree air that is passing over the coil. This sensible heat transfer will cause the temperature of the liquid refrigerant to cool down below the condenser saturation temperature. This process is called subcooling.

Condenser subcooling is defined as the amount of sensible heat that is given up in the condenser coil after all of the vapor has condensed.

The amount of condenser subcooling is determined, in part, by the point at which the last bit of vapor is present in the condenser coil. If there is vapor close to the outlet of the condenser coil, the amount of condenser subcooling will be low. However, if the last bit of vapor is closer to the inlet of the condenser coil, the amount of condenser subcooling will be higher. The higher the condenser subcooling the lower the temperature of the liquid refrigerant at the outlet of the condenser coil.

Condenser subcooling can be calculated by subtracting the condenser outlet temperature from the condenser saturation temperature:

$$\frac{\text{Condenser Saturation Temperature} - \text{Condenser Outlet Temperature}}{\text{Condenser Subcooling}}$$

Consider the R-410A condenser in Figure 27. The high side pressure in the system is 364.8 psig, the condenser saturation temperature is 110°F, and the condenser outlet temperature is 90°F. In this case the refrigerant is entering the condenser coil at a temperature of 175°F.

In this situation, the refrigerant at the inlet of the condenser is a superheated vapor. We know this because the saturation temperature that corresponds to the saturation pressure of 364.8 psig is 110°F, not 175°F. So, the superheated vapor must first desuperheat 65 degrees down to a temperature of 110°F before it can begin to condense.

At the outlet of the condenser, we have subcooled liquid. We know that this is the case, since the condenser outlet temperature of 90°F is lower than the saturation temperature of 110°F.

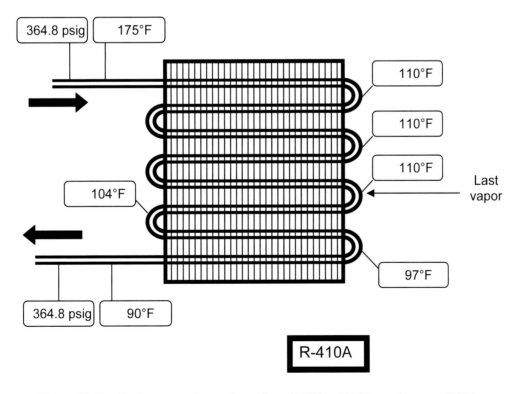

Figure 27. Hot discharge gas desuperheats from 175°F to 110°F, condenses at 110°F and then subcools from 110°F to 90°F.

31

Example #14

Consider the condenser in Figure 27. The system refrigerant is R-410A, the condenser saturation temperature is 110°F and the condenser outlet temperature is 90°F. Calculate the amount of subcooling in the condenser.

Solution:

Using the subcooling formula we get:

Condenser subcooling = Condenser Saturation Temp – Condenser Outlet Temp
Condenser subcooling = 110°F – 90°F
Condenser subcooling = 20°F

Example #15

Consider an R-22 condenser operating with a high side pressure of 260 psig and a condenser outlet of 100°F. Calculate the condenser subcooling.

Solution:

Since we have the condenser saturation pressure, we need to convert that temperature to a saturation pressure. Using the temperature/pressure chart, we convert our 260 psig pressure to a saturation temperature of 120°F.

Using the subcooling formula we get:

Condenser subcooling = Condenser Saturation Temp – Condenser Outlet Temp
Condenser subcooling = 120°F – 100°F
Condenser subcooling = 20°F

Just as we provided our deserted island example for conveying the concept of superheat, the same island can be used to express condenser subcooling. Assume that we are still on the same island but this time a submarine passes by. The submarine is submerged under the surface of the water, Figure 28.

Here are the analogies that can be made:

- The subcooling process takes place on the liquid side of the system, just as our submarine travels in the water.
- Subcooling calculations use the condenser saturation temperature which is higher than the condenser outlet temperature, just as the submarine is traveling below the surface of the water. Remember that the surface of the water represents the saturation temperature

32

- *Sub*-cooling → *Sub*-marine
- The submarine represents the outlet of the condenser
- In order to determine how far below the surface of the water the submarine is traveling, we need to determine the distance between the submarine and the water/air (saturation) line, just as we calculate condenser subcooling by determining the difference between the condenser saturation temperature and the condenser outlet temperature.

Figure 28. Subcooling analogy.

THE BASIC REFRIGERATION CYCLE

Putting it Together

Figure 29 represents a complete air conditioning system that operates with R-22 as its refrigerant. The system conditions are as follows:

- High side pressure 243 psig
- Condenser saturation temperature 115°F (from t/p chart)
- Low side pressure 68.5 psig
- Evaporator saturation temperature 40°F (from t/p chart)
- Condenser outlet temperature 95°F
- Evaporator outlet temperature 50°F
- Compressor discharge temperature 220°F

To conclude this portion of the text, we will follow one complete path around the system, referencing the parameters that were discussed thus far. In addition, alternative names for devices, components and lines are included for the sake of completeness.

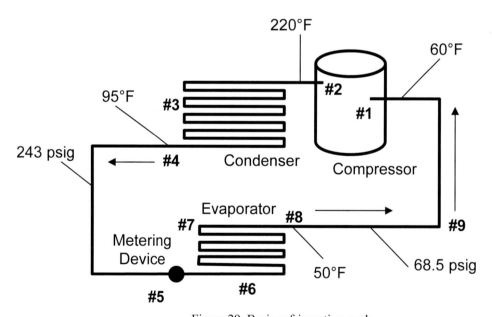

Figure 29. Basic refrigeration cycle.

Beginning at point #1, we have a low pressure, low temperature superheated vapor entering the compressor via the suction line. The suction line is the line that carries refrigerant from the evaporator back to the compressor. We know that the refrigerant is superheated since the temperature of the refrigerant (60°F) is higher than the evaporator saturation temperature of 40°F.

The vapor refrigerant is compressed in the compressor, where the temperature and pressure of the refrigerant are increased. Although both the temperature and pressure of the refrigerant are increased, it is important to remember that, since the refrigerant is superheated, there is no temperature/pressure relationship. High pressure, high temperature superheated (220°F) vapor refrigerant is then discharged from the compressor at point #2. The refrigerant vapor at this point is also referred to as discharge gas and the refrigerant line that carries the refrigerant from the compressor is called the discharge line or the hot gas line.

Although the temperature of the discharge gas is higher than the condenser saturation temperature, the high side pressure remains at 243 psig. The high side pressure is also referred to as the head pressure or discharge pressure.

The discharge vapor from the compressor immediately begins to cool, giving up sensible heat, as the surrounding air temperature is lower than the 220°F vapor temperature. So, as the hot gas travels from the compressor to the condenser, the refrigerant is desuperheating down to the condenser saturation temperature.

Once the vapor refrigerant has completely desuperheated and is at the condenser saturation temperature (115°F in this case), the refrigerant begins its vapor-to-liquid latent heat transfer at point #3. During the condensing process, the temperature remains constant at the condenser saturation temperature, but the liquid/vapor percentages in the saturated mixture change from more vapor and less liquid to more liquid and less vapor. This latent heat transfer continues until the refrigerant is 100% liquid at a temperature equal to the condenser saturation temperature of 115°F.

The liquid leaves the condenser at point #4 as a high temperature, high pressure subcooled liquid. We know that the refrigerant is subcooled because the temperature of the liquid at the outlet of the condenser (95°F) is lower than the condenser saturation temperature of 115°F. The amount of subcooling is equal to the condenser saturation temperature minus the condenser outlet temperature, 115°F - 95°F, which is equal to 20°F. The subcooling process is a sensible heat transfer.

The subcooled liquid travels from the condenser to the metering device in the liquid line.

At the metering device, #5, also referred to as the expansion device, refrigerant is fed into the evaporator as a low pressure, low temperature saturated liquid. As the liquid refrigerant flows through and leaves the metering device, a portion of the liquid vaporizes, or flashes, into a vapor. So, the state of the refrigerant at the inlet of the evaporator is roughly an 80%-20% liquid-vapor mix.

The refrigerant in the evaporator, #6, is at a pressure of 68.5 psig. This pressure is often referred to as the low side pressure, suction pressure or back pressure. The saturated refrigerant is vaporizing at a temperature of 40°F (from the temperature/pressure chart). The evaporating process is a latent heat transfer and continues until the refrigerant has completely vaporized.

Once completely vaporized, the 40-degree vapor continues to absorb heat from the air passing over the coil, causing the temperature of the vapor to increase. This process is a sensible heat transfer and is called superheat. The amount of superheat in this evaporator is equal to the evaporator outlet temperature, #8, minus the evaporator saturation temperature, 50°F - 40°F, or 10 degrees.

This superheated vapor at the outlet of the evaporator flows onto the compressor through the suction line. In this example, the refrigerant picks up an additional 10 degrees of superheat in the suction line as the refrigerant leaves the evaporator at 50°F and enters the compressor at a temperature of 60°F.

THE PRESSURE ENTHALPY CHART

What Do All of Those Lines Mean?

At first glance, the pressure enthalpy diagram, also known as the Mollier (sometimes spelled Molier or Moliere) diagram or chart, Figure 29, can be somewhat intimidating. There are a large number of lines and curves that can cause ones eyes to cross if the attempt is made to completely understand the entire chart at once. The purpose of this first section is, therefore, to help the reader gain an understanding of the chart, one line at a time.

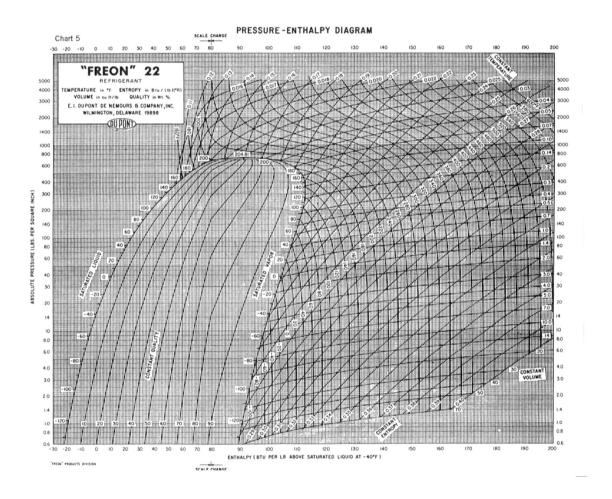

Figure 29. An R-22 pressure enthalpy chart. Courtesy DuPont.

We will first examine the units that are used on the horizontal and vertical scales, Figure 30. The vertical scale on the pressure-enthalpy chart represents the system pressures in psia. When system pressures are obtained, they are in psig. These psig readings must first be converted to psia before they can be plotted on the pressure-enthalpy chart. Please refer to pages 19 and 20 for the methods used to convert gauge readings to the required absolute pressures. The horizontal scale on the chart represents the heat content, or enthalpy, of the refrigerant in btu/lb. The btu/lb units indicate the amount of heat energy, in btu, that one pound of refrigerant at those conditions contains. As refrigerant moves from the left to the right, the heat content of the refrigerant increases and, as the refrigerant moves from right to left, the heat content decreases, Figure 31. So having the system pressures on the y-axis and the heat content (enthalpy) on the x-axis, we now have our pressure enthalpy chart. The chart is also referred to as the *p-e chart*, for pressure enthalpy or the *p-h chart*, where the "h" is the letter used to denote enthalpy. Some like to refer to the p-h chart as a pressure heat chart.

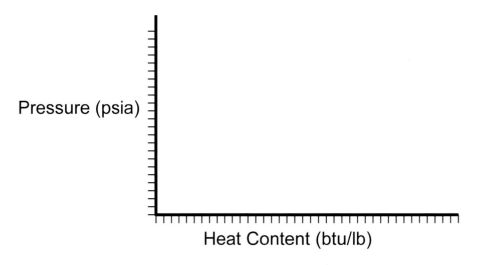

Figure 30. The pressure enthalpy chart plots pressure (vertical axis) against heat content (horizontal axis).

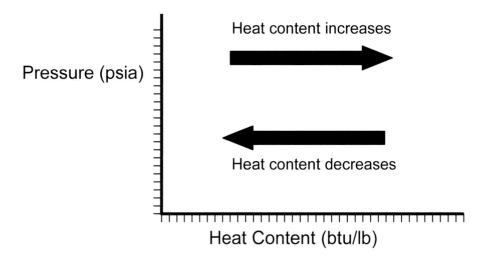

Figure 31. The heat content of the refrigerant increases as it moves from left to right and decreases as it moves from right to left.

The horizontal lines on the chart represent lines of constant pressure, Figure 32. As we move in a horizontal path across the chart, the pressure remains constant even though the heat content changes, as shown back in Figure 31.

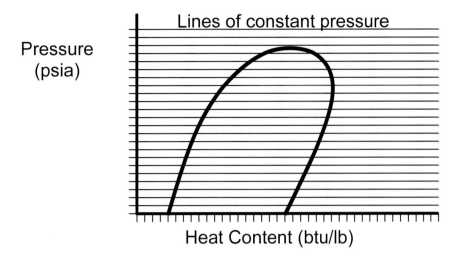

Figure 32. Lines of constant pressure run horizontally across the chart.

The Vertical lines on the chart represent lines of constant enthalpy or constant heat content, Figure 33. As we move in a vertical path through the chart, the heat content, in btu/lb, remains constant even though the system pressure changes.

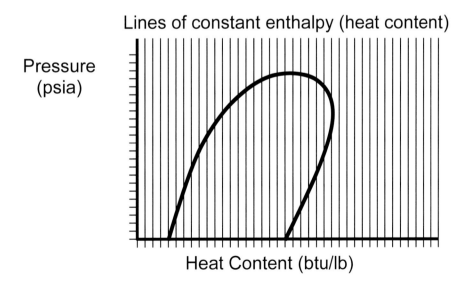

Figure 33. Lines of constant enthalpy run vertically across the chart.

The curve on the pressure-enthalpy chart represents saturated refrigerant, Figure 34. Refrigerant that is on or under this curve is saturated and follows the pressure/ temperature relationship for that refrigerant. Refrigerant that is not under the curve is either a superheated vapor or a subcooled liquid, depending on its location on the chart. When refrigerant is *on* the left side of the saturation curve, the refrigerant is a 100 percent saturated liquid, while refrigerant *on* the right side of the curve is a 100 percent saturated vapor. As refrigerant moves horizontally under the curve, the saturation temperature and pressure remains the same, while the heat content and quality of the refrigerant changes.

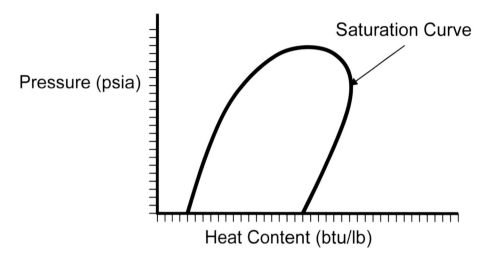

Figure 34. The saturation curve on the pressure enthalpy chart. Only refrigerant under this curve is saturated and follows the pressure/temperature relationship.

Refrigerant quality refers to the percentage of liquid and vapor in the saturated mixture. Under the saturation curve are nine steep lines that represent the percentage of liquid/vapor refrigerant that is present. The leftmost quality line under the curve represents refrigerant that is 90 percent liquid and 10 percent vapor. The line to the right of this line represents refrigerant that is 80 percent liquid and 20 percent vapor. The rightmost line under the curve represents refrigerant that is 90 percent vapor and 10 percent liquid, Figure 35. The closer the refrigerant is to the edge of the saturation curve, the closer the refrigerant is to becoming a 100% saturated refrigerant.

Side note:

> If the conditions of a refrigerant fall on the *left* side of the saturation curve itself, any *removal* of heat will cause the refrigerant to change from a saturated liquid to a subcooled liquid.

> If the conditions of a refrigerant fall on the *right* side of the saturation curve itself, any *addition* of heat will cause the refrigerant to change from a saturated vapor to a superheated vapor.

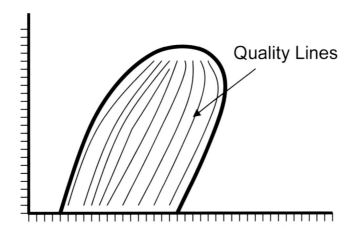

Figure 35. The refrigerant quality lines under the saturation curve.

When refrigerant is not under the curve, the refrigerant is either a superheated vapor or a subcooled liquid. When the refrigerant is to the left of the saturation curve, the refrigerant is a subcooled liquid and when the refrigerant is to the right of the saturation curve, the refrigerant is a superheated vapor, Figure 36. Remember that when refrigerant is either a superheated vapor or a subcooled liquid, the refrigerant does not follow the pressure/temperature relationship.

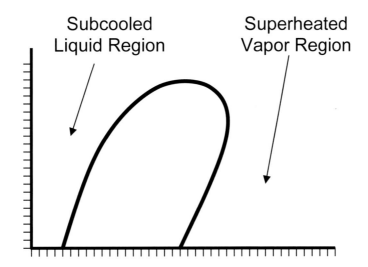

Figure 36. Refrigerant to the left of the saturation curve is a subcooled liquid, while refrigerant to the right of the curve is a superheated vapor.

The horizontal lines under the saturation curve represent lines of constant temperature, Figure 37. As the refrigerant moves along one of these lines, either to the left or to the right, the temperature and pressure of the refrigerant remains constant, but the heat content and the quality of the refrigerant changes. As refrigerant moves to the right, the heat content of the refrigerant increases, the percentage of liquid present decreases and the percentage of vapor increases. This is an example of what is taking place in the evaporator of the air conditioning or refrigeration system. As refrigerant moves to the left along one of the constant temperature lines under the saturation curve, the heat content of

41

the refrigerant decreases and the percentage of vapor refrigerant present decreases. This is what is taking place in the system condenser.

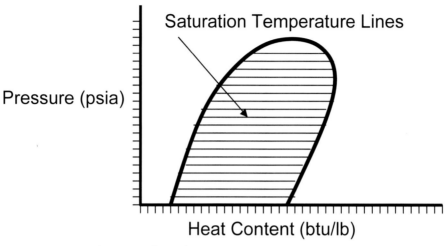

Figure 37. Lines of constant temperature under the saturation curve.

Side note:

It should be mentioned here that, for single component refrigerants such as R-12, R-22, R-134a, the constant temperature lines under the saturation curve are perfectly horizontal as there is only one saturation temperature that corresponds to a given saturation pressure. On the other hand, when we are dealing with blended refrigerants that operate with a temperature glide, the constant temperature lines under the saturation curve will be angled, as in the case of R-407C, Figure 38.

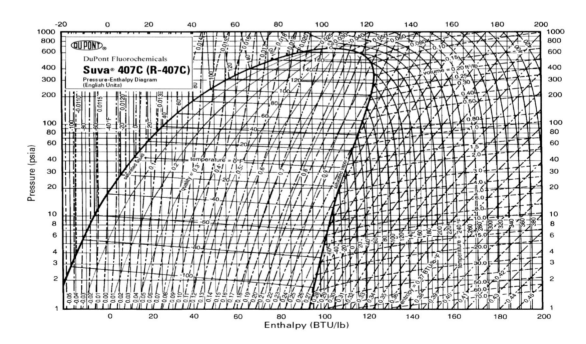

Figure 38. Blended refrigerants that operate with a temperature glide have angled constant temperature lines under the saturation curve. Courtesy DuPont.

The lines of constant temperature extend both to the left and to the right of the saturation curve, Figure 39. Notice that the lines of constant temperature to the left and to the right of the saturation curve are not horizontal lines. This means that as refrigerant moves along one of these lines, a change in pressure results. Since the pressure changes while the temperature remains constant, the pressure/temperature relationship does not hold.

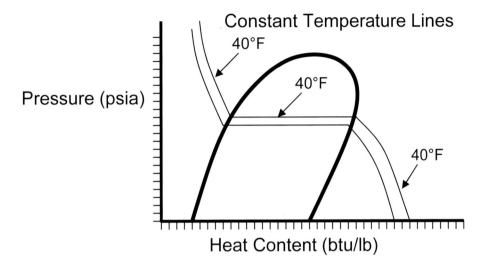

Figure 39. Constant temperature lines extend into the subcooled liquid and superheated vapor regions of the chart.

On the vapor side of the saturation curve, the set of steep lines represent lines of constant entropy, Figure 40. These lines represent heat content in btu/lb per degree. Since the pressure-enthalpy chart is based on absolute pressures (psia), the temperatures referenced on the entropy lines are absolute temperatures, namely those on the Rankin scale. The lines of constant entropy are commonly used to represent the compression process.

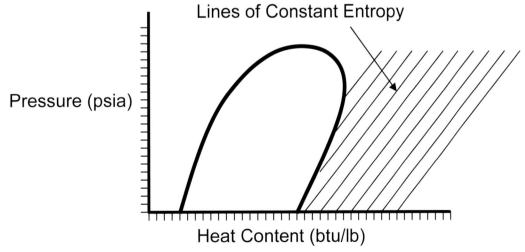

Figure 40. Lines of constant entropy

On the superheated vapor side of the pressure-enthalpy chart, the set of near-horizontal slanted lines represents lines of constant volume, Figure 41. Constant volume, or specific volume, represents the number of cubic feet per pound of refrigerant that are required to make up one pound of refrigerant. As the specific volume increases, the number of cubic feet required to make up one pound of refrigerant increases and the density of the refrigerant decreases. As the specific volume decreases, the number of cubic feet of refrigerant required to make up one pound decreases and the density of the refrigerant increases. We often use the specific volume of the refrigerant at the inlet of the compressor, point "D", to determine the amount (volume) of refrigerant that is being processed by the compressor per minute. The volumetric capacity of the compressor is given in ft^3/min, or cubic feet per minute.

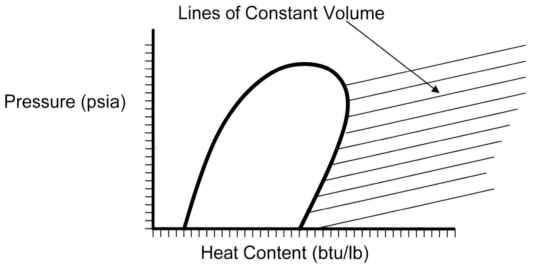

Figure 41. Lines of constant volume.

Side note:

Point "D" as well as the other relevant points on the pressure enthalpy chart will be discussed in later sections.

44

THE PRESSURE ENTHALPY CHART

The Basic Refrigeration Cycle and the Pressure Enthalpy Chart

Let us recall the four major system components as well as the state of the refrigerant as it flows through the system. As we do this, we will reference the pressure enthalpy chart as we begin to construct the completed system plot.

Looking back at the graphic representation of the refrigeration cycle, we concluded that the condenser was the system component that was located at the top of our square, Figure 42.

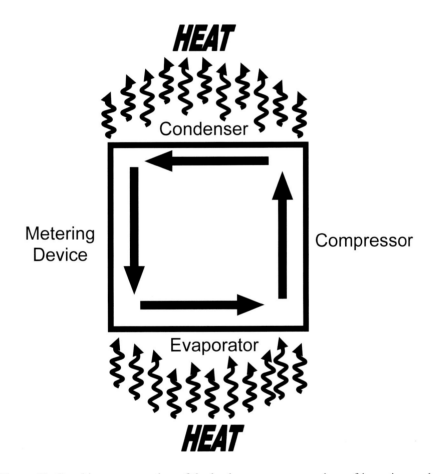

Figure 42. Graphic representation of the basic vapor-compression refrigeration cycle.

We should also recall that there are three mini processes that take place in the condenser; namely desuperheating, condensing and subcooling. From our initial discussion of the pressure enthalpy chart, we established the following:

- Superheated refrigerant was located to the right of the saturation curve
- Saturated refrigerant was found on and under the saturation curve
- Subcooled liquid was found to the left of the saturation curve

In the condenser, refrigerant can be found in all three states, so the line that represents the condenser should pass through all three regions of the chart, Figure 43.

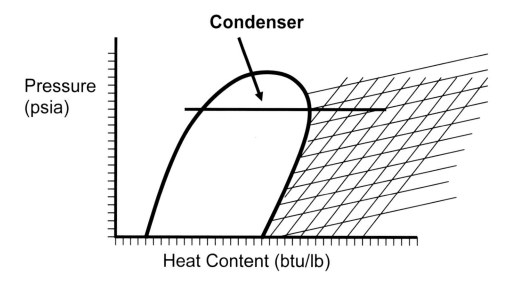

Figure 43. The line that represents the condenser passes through the subcooled liquid, saturated and superheated vapor regions of the pressure enthalpy chart.

Since the condenser is the system component that is responsible for rejecting heat, the direction of refrigerant flow through the condenser, as represented in Figure 43, is from right to left. The right end of the line represents the point where the discharge gas from the compressor enters the discharge line as a superheated vapor. As the refrigerant moves to the left, it desuperheats until it reaches the right side of the saturation curve. Still moving from right to left, the refrigerant undergoes its latent, vapor-to-liquid change of state. This continues until the left side of the saturation curve is reached. The left portion of the condenser line represents the subcooling process where the liquid refrigerant is cooled to a temperature below the refrigerant's saturation temperature.

From the condenser, the high pressure, high temperature subcooled liquid travels to the metering device. The metering device takes the high pressure subcooled liquid and facilitates the change of state to a low pressure, low temperature saturated liquid. So, on the pressure enthalpy chart, the metering device is represented by a vertical line that passes through the subcooled liquid and saturated refrigerant regions, Figure 44. The refrigerant will follow a path from top to bottom as it flows through the metering device as the pressure at the outlet of the device is low, while the pressure at the inlet of the component is high.

Side note:

The process that takes place in the metering device referred to as an adiabatic process, as the temperature and pressure of the substance is reduced, but the heat content, in btu/lb, remains the same.

46

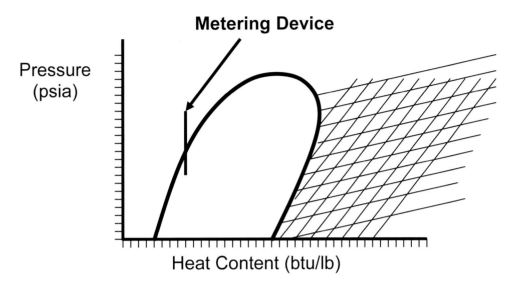

Figure 44. The metering device line passes through the subcooled and saturated refrigerant regions.

The evaporator facilitates the state of change from a saturated liquid to a superheated vapor, so the line that represents the evaporator must pass through the saturated and superheated refrigerant regions on the pressure enthalpy chart, Figure 45.

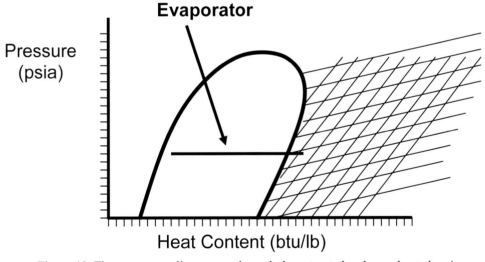

Figure 45. The evaporator line passes through the saturated and superheated regions.

Once the refrigerant leaves the evaporator as a low pressure, low temperature superheated vapor, the suction line carries the refrigerant back to the compressor. In the suction line, however, additional superheat is added to the refrigerant. So, if we examine the suction line, refrigerant enters the line as a superheated vapor and leaves the line (enters the compressor) at a higher superheated temperature. The pressure at the inlet and outlet of the suction line remains the same, Figure 46.

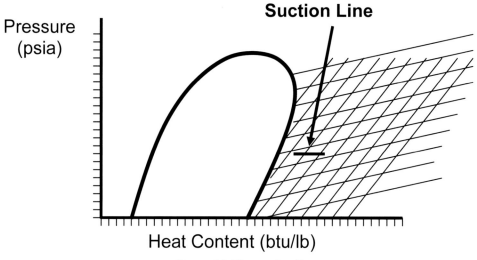

Figure 46. The suction line.

From the suction line we enter the compressor. Refrigerant enters the compressor as a low pressure, low temperature superheated vapor and leaves the compressor as a high pressure, high temperature superheated vapor. As the refrigerant undergoes the compression process, the pressure, temperature and heat content of the refrigerant all increase. The line that represents the compressor is shown in Figure 47.

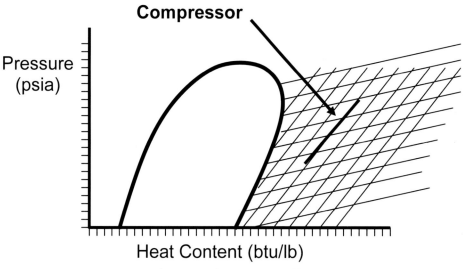

Figure 47. The compressor line.

Since one mini process begins where the previous process ended, the lines representing the individual mini processes must be connected in a head to tail fashion to create the repeating, vapor compression cycle. Therefore, a completed plot of an air conditioning system will look similar to that as shown in figure 48.

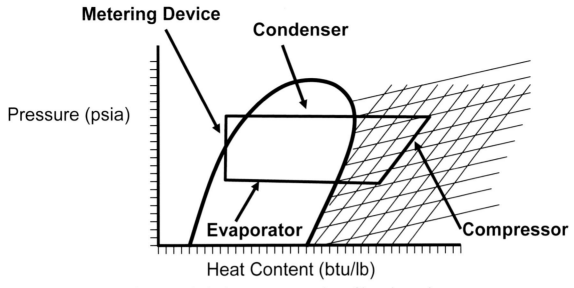

Figure 48. The basic, vapor compression refrigeration cycle
on the pressure enthalpy chart.

We have labeled the key points on the pressure-enthalpy chart "A" through "E", Figure 49. Point "A" is located in the subcooled refrigerant region and represents the outlet of the condenser and the inlet of the metering device as well as the liquid line itself. Point "B" represents the outlet of the metering device and the inlet of the evaporator. Refrigerant at point "B" is saturated. Point "C" represents the outlet of the evaporator and the beginning of the suction line. Point "D" is the end of the suction line and the inlet of the compressor and point "E" is the outlet of the compressor and the beginning of the discharge line and condenser. The state of the refrigerant at points "C", "D" and "E" is a superheated vapor.

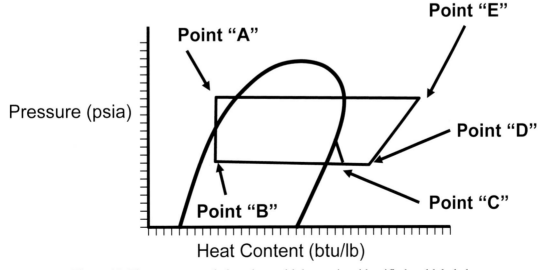

Figure 49. The pressure enthalpy chart with key points identified and labeled.

Here is a summary of the points, system components and the state of the refrigerant as it moves from point to point on the chart:

POINTS	COMPONENT	PROCESS(ES)	STATE(S)
"A" to "B"	Metering Device	Lowering pressure	SL to SR
"B" to "C"	Evaporator	Absorbing heat	SR to SV
"C" to "D"	Suction Line	N/A	SV to SV
"D" to "E"	Compressor	Increasing pressure	SV to SV
"E" to "A"	Condenser	Rejecting heat	SV to SR to SL

Where   SL = Subcooled liquid
                     SR = Saturated refrigerant
                     SV = Superheated vapor

Side note:

        If the suction line is relatively short and well insulated, points "C" and "D" can actually be the same point. This condition is desirable as sensible heat picked up in the suction line decreases the efficiency and effectiveness of system operation.

PRESSURE ENTHALPY: SYSTEM CHARACTERISTICS

Net Refrigeration Effect (NRE)

The main purpose of an air conditioning or refrigeration system is to provide comfort cooling or refrigeration. The amount of cooling a system produces is directly related to the amount of heat that the refrigerant in the evaporator can absorb. The amount of heat that can be absorbed in the evaporator is, in turn, related to the amount of refrigerant that is flowing through the evaporator coil as well as the number of btus of heat energy the refrigerant can hold.

Under different sets of conditions, the refrigerant's ability to absorb heat energy (btus) will change. So, conditions external to the system, such as a dirty air filter or excessively warm outside ambient temperatures, will have definite effects on system performance. The net refrigeration effect, NRE, provides us with the amount of heat, in btu/lb, that the refrigerant absorbs in the evaporator. The NRE takes into account the amount of heat present in the refrigerant as it enters the evaporator as well as the amount of heat present in the refrigerant as it exits the coil. The larger the NRE, the greater the heat transfer rate per pound of refrigerant circulated. *I like to think of the NRE as the size of a sponge that absorbs btus. The larger the sponge, the more btus can be held by it. The larger the NRE the more btus can be absorbed by the pound of refrigerant.*

Point "B" on the pressure-enthalpy plot represents the heat content of the refrigerant at the inlet of the evaporator and point "C" represents the heat content of the refrigerant at the outlet of the evaporator. The difference between these two values yields the amount of heat absorbed by the evaporator. So,

Net Refrigeration Effect, NRE = Heat content at point "C" – Heat content at point "B"

Example #16:

Consider the pressure enthalpy plot in Figure 50. The heat content at the inlet of the evaporator is 40 btu/lb and the heat content at the outlet of the evaporator is 110 btu/lb. Calculate the NRE for this evaporator.

Solution:

The refrigerant at the inlet of the evaporator has a heat content of 40 btu/lb and leaves the evaporator with a heat content of 110 btu/lb. The NRE is the difference between the heat content of the inlet (point "B" on the plot) and the outlet of the evaporator (point "C" on the plot):

NRE = Heat content at point "C" - Heat content at point "B"
NRE = 110 btu/lb – 40 btu/lb
NRE = 70 btu/lb

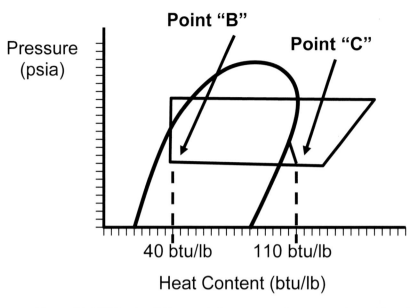

Figure 50. NRE is the difference in heat content between points "B" and "C".

Example #17:

Consider an evaporator that is operating with a NRE of 85 btu/lb. What is the heat content of the refrigerant, in btu/lb, at the outlet of the evaporator if the heat content at the inlet of the coil is 35 btu/lb?

Solution:

Since we know that the heat content of the refrigerant at the inlet of the coil (point "B") is 35 btu/lb and the refrigerant absorbed 85 btu/lb in the coil, the heat content at the outlet of the coil (point "C") can be calculated by adding the NRE to the heat content at the inlet of the coil:

NRE = Heat content at point "C" - Heat content at point "B"

Or

Heat content at point "C" = NRE + Heat content at point "B"
Heat content at point "C" = 85 btu/lb + 35 btu/lb
Heat content at point "C" = 120 btu/lb

You can double check your answer by using the original formula:

NRE = Heat content at point "C" - Heat content at point "B"
NRE = 120 btu/lb – 35 btu/lb
NRE = 85 btu/lb

PRESSURE ENTHALPY: SYSTEM CHARACTERISTICS

Mass Flow Rate per Ton (MFR/ton)

Having just discussed the NRE, we know that one pound of refrigerant will have the ability to hold a certain number of btus under a certain set of system operating conditions. A high NRE indicates a large amount of heat absorbed by the refrigerant and a low NRE indicates that the refrigerant is not absorbing as much heat.

When we transfer 12,000 btus in a one hour period, we say that we have one ton of refrigeration. Since 12,000 btus per hour (btuh) is equal to one ton, we can also argue that 200 btus per minute is the same as one ton:

$$12,000 \text{ btu/hr} \quad x \quad 1 \text{ hour/60 min} \ = 200 \text{ btu/min}$$

So, in order to obtain one ton of refrigeration we have to transfer 200 btu/min. From our NRE, we know how many btus can be absorbed by each pound of refrigerant. For example, if our NRE is equal to 200 btu/lb, we will have to move one pound of refrigerant per minute to obtain one ton of refrigeration. If the NRE was only 100 btu/lb, we would have to move two pounds of refrigerant in one minute to obtain one ton of refrigeration. Let's take a look at the following chart to clarify the point:

NRE	One Ton of Refrigeration	Required Refrigerant Flow
200 btu/lb	200 btu/min	1 lb/min
100 btu/lb	200 btu/min	2 lb/min
50 btu/lb	200 btu/min	4 lb/min
25 btu/lb	200 btu/min	8 lb/min
20 btu/lb	200 btu/min	10 lb/min
10 btu/lb	200 btu/min	20 lb/min
5 btu/lb	200 btu/min	40 lb/min
4 btu/lb	200 btu/min	50 lb/min
2 btu/lb	200 btu/min	100 lb/min
1 btu/lb	200 btu/min	200 lb/min

It can be seen from this chart that, as the btu absorbing capacity of each pound of refrigerant, NRE, decreases, the number of pounds of refrigerant that must be circulated to obtain the same one ton of refrigeration increases. In plain English, *larger NREs allow us to obtain larger system capacities while circulating less refrigerant through the system.*

The Mass Flow Rate per Ton can, therefore, be calculated by dividing 200 by the NRE.

Example #18

Consider an evaporator that has a heat content of 40 btu/lb at its inlet and a heat content of 120 btu/lb at its outlet. What is the Mass Flow Rate per Ton for this system?

Solution:

Mass Flow Rate per Ton = 200 btu/min ÷ NRE (btu/lb)

The NRE for this evaporator is equal to 80 btu/lb (120 btu/lb – 40 btu/lb)

Mass Flow Rate per Ton = 200 btu/min ÷ 80 btu/lb

Mass Flow Rate per Ton = 2.5 lb/min/ton

So, if there is an actual refrigerant flow through the system of 2.5 lb/min, the system will be providing one ton of refrigeration. If the system was flowing refrigerant at a rate of 5 lb/min, the system will be providing two tons of refrigeration, and so on.

We can then conclude that a lower Mass Flow Rate per Ton is an indication of higher system efficiency. This is mainly because the compressor will have to move less refrigerant at a lower MFR/ton to obtain each ton of refrigeration. We obtain a lower MFR/ton from a higher NRE.

Side note:

In addition to other factors, we lose system efficiency when an evaporator freezes up due to, for example, a dirty air filter. The dirty air filter reduces the amount of air passing over the evaporator coil, causing the saturation temperature and pressure of the refrigerant to drop. Because of the pressure enthalpy chart configuration, a reduction in saturation pressure and temperature (with all other things remaining equal) will result in a lower NRE. A lower NRE leads to a higher MFR/ton, which means that the compressor will have to pump more refrigerant through the system to maintain the original system capacity.

PRESSURE ENTHALPY: SYSTEM CHARACTERISTICS

Heat of Work (HOW)

The Heat of Work, HOW, represents the amount of heat absorbed into the system from the time the refrigerant enters the compressor until the refrigerant is discharged from the compressor. The refrigerant enters the compressor at point "D" and leaves the compressor at point "E" on the pressure enthalpy chart, Figure 51. The difference between the heat content at these two points yields the amount of heat absorbed into the system during the compression process. This heat is partly due to the process of refrigerant compression and also due in part to the heat generated by the friction between the rubbing surfaces inside the compressor. *Note: According to ASHRAE, this system characteristic is referred to as the Heat of Compression, HOC. The term HOW is being used to separate the heat absorbed into the system via the suction line, since the "saturated" cycle used by ASHRAE does not reflect suction line superheat.*

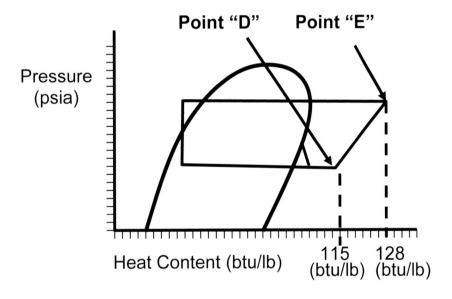

Figure 51. Heat of work is calculated from the compressor inlet to the compressor outlet.

The heat of work, as defined above, is generated in the compressor as indicated by the line on the pressure enthalpy plot that represents the compressor. This line follows, for the most part, a line of constant entropy, which is the rate at which heat is absorbed by the refrigerant in btu/lb/degree. The "degree" in the entropy units are on the Rankine temperature scale on which 0 degrees Fahrenheit is equal to 460 degrees Rankine and 0 degrees Rankine is equal to -460°F.

Heat of Work can be calculated by the following formula:

Heat of Work, HOW = Heat content at point "E" – Heat content at point "D"

Example #19:

Consider the system plotted in Figure 51. Calculate the Heat of Work for this system.

Solution:

From the figure, we can see that the heat content at point "E" is 128 btu/lb and the heat content at point "D" is 115 btu/lb. Using the formula for Heat of Work, we get:

Heat of Work, HOW = Heat content at point "E" – Heat content at point "D"
Heat of Work, HOW = 128 btu/lb - 115 btu/lb
Heat of Work, HOW = 13 btu/lb

Side note:

By inspecting the pressure enthalpy plot it can be seen that, as the distance between the high side pressure line and the low side pressure line becomes greater, the HOW for that system will increase. This makes sense because the compressor has to do more work to increase the pressure of the refrigerant when the difference between the two pressures is great. This will translate directly to more heat being generated and transferred to the refrigerant, Figure 52a. Conversely, when the high side pressure and the low side pressure are closer together, the HOW is smaller as less work must be done to increase and decrease the pressure of the refrigerant in the system.

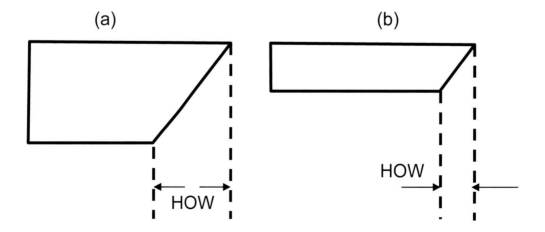

Figure 52. (a) Heat of work is larger when the difference between system pressures is large. (b) Heat of work is smaller when the difference between system pressures is small.

PRESSURE ENTHALPY: SYSTEM CHARACTERISTICS

Compression Ratio (CR)

Having just covered the Heat of Work, we are well aware that the system pressures (high and low) as well as the difference between the two, play an important role in determining the effectiveness and efficiency of the system. For this reason, there must be some means to rate the relationship that exists between the system pressures. This relationship is called the compression ratio. In a nutshell, the compression ratio provides us with information regarding how much higher the head pressure is than the system suction pressure.

The compression ratio is an indicator of system performance. The result from the following calculation indicates how many times higher the head pressure is than the suction or back pressure. For a properly operating R-22 or R-410A high temperature refrigeration (air conditioning) system at design conditions, the compression ratio should be in the range of 3:1. Excessively high compression ratios indicate that there is an increased heat of work, which will lead to other system problems that will be addressed shortly.

The formula for compression ratio is:

Compression Ratio = High Side Pressure (psia) ÷ Low Side Pressure (psia)

Note that the pressures that are used are absolute pressures, so our gauge readings must be converted to absolute pressures in order to use the formula. Refer back to pages 19 and 20 for the pressure conversions.

Example #20:

Consider an R-22 air conditioning system that is operating with a high side pressure of 240 psia and a low side pressure of 80 psia. Determine the compression ratio for this system and decide if the compression ratio is acceptable.

Solution:

Using the compression ratio formula, we get:

Compression Ratio = High Side Pressure (psia) ÷ Low Side Pressure (psia)
Compression Ratio = 240 psia ÷ 80 psia
Compression Ratio = 3:1

For high temperature refrigeration (air conditioning), this compression ratio is desirable and well within acceptable limits.

Example #21:

Consider an R-22 air conditioning system that is operating with a high side pressure of 260 psig and a low side pressure of 50 psig. The system is equipped with a head pressure control designed to maintain the discharge pressure at 260 psig. The system is operating with a clogged air filter. Calculate the compression ratio for this system.

Solution:

Since the pressures are given as gauge pressures, the readings must first be converted to absolute values. From page 19, we know that we can convert gauge pressures above 0 psig to absolute pressures by adding 15 to the gauge pressures:

High side pressure in psia = 260 psig + 15
High side pressure in psia = 275 psia

Low side pressure in psia = 50 psig + 15
Low side pressure in psia = 65 psia

Compression Ratio = High Side Pressure (psia) ÷ Low Side Pressure (psia)
Compression Ratio = 275 psia ÷ 65 psia
Compression Ratio = 4.23:1

This compression ratio is higher than the design compression ratio of 3:1 so a problem should be suspected.

Side note:

The 3:1 recommended range is for high temperature refrigeration (air conditioning) systems that operate with R-22 or R-410A as the system refrigerant. High temperature refrigeration systems that operate with R-407C, for example, operate at slightly higher compression ratios (3.1:1 to 3.8:1) at design conditions.

Side note:

Medium and low temperature refrigeration systems operate with higher compression ratios, given the lower evaporator saturation temperatures and pressures. The best way to determine the ideal compression ratio for a given system is to:

1. Determine the design condenser saturation temperature and the design evaporator saturation temperature for the system
2. Convert these temperatures to pressures with a temperature/pressure chart.
3. Convert the gauge pressure readings to absolute readings
4. Divide the high side pressure by the low side pressure

Example #22:

What would be the ideal compression ratio for a standard efficiency R-134a medium temperature refrigeration system that is designed to operate with an outside ambient temperature of 90°F and an evaporator coil temperature of 25°F?

Solution:

With a standard efficiency condenser, the condenser saturation temperature will be roughly 30 degrees higher than the outside ambient temperature. Since the design outside air temperature is 90°F, the design condenser saturation temperature is 120°F. From the pressure/temperature chart, the saturation pressure on the high side of the system will be 171.2 psig. By adding 15 to this pressure, we get an absolute pressure of about 186 psia.

If the evaporator saturation temperature is 25°F, the corresponding gauge pressure is about 22 psig, or 37 psia.

The compression ratio can be found by using the formula:

Compression Ratio = High Side Pressure (psia) ÷ Low Side Pressure (psia)
Compression Ratio = 186 psia ÷ 37 psia
Compression Ratio = 5.03:1

Side note:

It pays to note that a ***high compression ratio results in a high heat of work***. The high heat of work, in turn, means that more heat is being introduced to the system. This additional heat must later be rejected by the condenser. System problems should be suspected if the compression ratio is high as in the following example.

Example #23:

Calculate the compression ratio of an R-134a system that is operating with a suction pressure of 12.4"Hg and a high side pressure of 135 psig.

We can convert the 12.4"Hg to an absolute pressure by the following (page 20):

psia = (30"Hg – Vacuum reading) ÷ 2
psia = (30"Hg – 12.4"Hg) ÷ 2
psia = 17.6 ÷ 2 = 8.8
12.4"Hg = 8.8 psia = 9 psia

The high side absolute pressure is 135 + 15 = 150 psia

The compression ratio is therefore equal to 150 psia ÷ 9 psia = 16.7:1

PRESSURE ENTHALPY: SYSTEM CHARACTERISTICS

Heat of Compression (HOC)

The Heat of Compression, HOC, represents the amount of heat absorbed into the system from the time the refrigerant leaves the evaporator until the refrigerant is discharged from the compressor. The refrigerant leaves the evaporator at point "C" and leaves the compressor at point "E", Figure 53. The difference between the heat content at these two points yields the amount of heat absorbed into the system in the suction line as well as during the compression process. *Note: The HOC term used here is different from that used by ASHRAE. ASHRAE's saturated refrigeration cycle does not take suction line superheat into account, which has a negative effect on system capacity, effectiveness and efficiency. The HOC term, as used here, includes the suction line superheat to give more accurate results when calculating the system's COP, efficiency and capacity.*

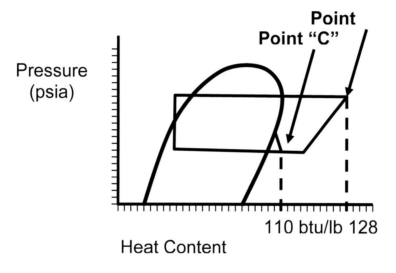

Figure 53. The heat of compression is picked up in the suction line as well as in the compressor and is located on the pressure enthalpy plot between points "C" and "E".

Heat of Compression can be calculated by the following formula:

Heat of Compression, HOC = Heat content at point "E" – Heat content at point "C"

Example #24:

Calculate the heat of compression, HOC, for the system plot in Figure 53.

Solution:

From the formula: HOC = Heat content at point "E" – Heat content at point "C"
HOC = 128 btu/lb – 110 btu/lb
HOC = 18 btu/lb

Side note:

The heat of compression can be thought of as all of the heat added to the refrigerant that does not contribute to the refrigeration effect. For example, heat picked up in the suction line does not help to cool the air conditioned or refrigerated space. All of the heat that contributed to the HOC must be rejected without a refrigeration benefit, so the portion of the condenser capacity that is used for this purpose is, in effect, lost.

Side note:

If the suction line of the system is short and the line is very well insulated, the amount of heat picked up in the suction line, between points "C" and "D" on the pressure enthalpy chart, may be very small or may actually be very close to zero. If such is the case, points "C" and "D" may be very close together or, ideally, be the same point altogether, Figure 54. If such is the case, the heat of compression, HOC, and the heat of work, HOW, will be the same.

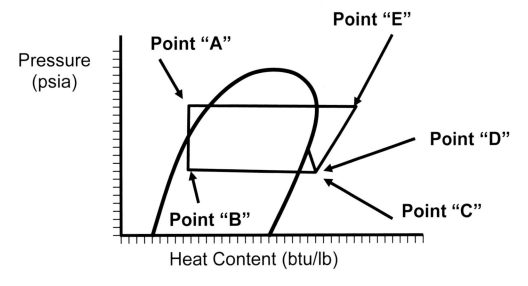

Figure 54. Negligible heat gain in the suction line causes point "C" and point "D" to become one in the same.

Example #25:

Consider the system in Figure 54. The heat content at point "C" is 110 btu/lb, the heat content at point "D" is 110 btu/lb and the heat content at point "E" is 128 btu/lb. Calculate the HOC and the HOW.

Solution:

Both the HOW and the HOC are 18 btu/lb for this system.

61

PRESSURE ENTHALPY: SYSTEM CHARACTERISTICS

Coefficient of Performance (COP)

Efficiency, in general, is determined by comparing the benefit received to the cost of the benefit. If the cost of the benefit is very low and the actual benefit received is great, we conclude that the process is worthwhile and will likely be repeated. If, on the other hand, the cost of a benefit is very high and the actual benefit is small, the likelihood of repeating that particular process is low.

We determine the efficiency of air conditioning and refrigeration systems in much the same way. The benefit we receive from an air conditioning system is the cooling effect, which, in the case of our pressure enthalpy chart, is the NRE. Refer back to pages 51 and 52 for a quick review of NRE if necessary.

The cost involved in obtaining the NRE is all of the heat that is absorbed into the system; namely our heat of compression, HOC.

The coefficient of performance of a system, COP, one measure of system efficiency, and is the ratio of realized output, NRE, as compared to the resources used to achieve that output, HOC. Therefore, the coefficient of performance is given by the following:

$$\text{Coefficient of Performance, COP} = \text{NRE} \div \text{HOC}$$

Example #26:

>   Consider an air conditioning system that is operating with a NRE of 72 btu/lb and an HOC of 18 btu/lb. Calculate the COP of the system.

Solution:

>   Using the formula for the coefficient of performance, we get:

>   Coefficient of Performance, COP = NRE ÷ HOC
>   Coefficient of Performance, COP = 72 btu/lb ÷ 18 btu/lb
>   Coefficient of Performance, COP = 4

Side note:

>   The larger the NRE and the smaller the HOC, the higher the COP. One of the easiest things that a service technician can do to help increase the efficiency of an air conditioning system is to make certain that all suction line insulation is properly installed and free from damage. Reducing the amount of heat absorbed by the suction line decreases the HOC and increases the COP.

Example #27:

Consider the pressure enthalpy plot in Figure 55. Determine the NRE, HOW, HOC and the COP for this system. Then provide two possible reasons for the difference between the HOW and the HOC.

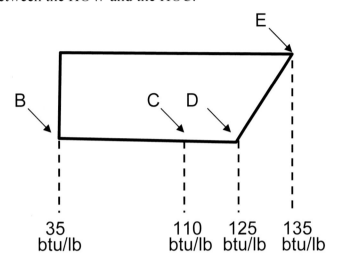

Figure 55. Example #27.

Solution:

NRE = Heat Content at Point "C" – Heat Content at Point "B"
NRE = 110 btu/lb - 35 btu/lb
NRE = 75 btu/lb

HOW = Heat Content at Point "E" – Heat Content at Point "D"
HOW = 135 btu/lb - 125 btu/lb
HOW = 10 btu/lb

HOC = Heat Content at Point "E" – Heat Content at Point "C"
HOC = 135 btu/lb - 110 btu/lb
HOC = 25 btu/lb

Coefficient of Performance, COP = NRE ÷ HOC
Coefficient of Performance, COP = 75 btu/lb ÷ 25 btu/lb
Coefficient of Performance, COP = 3

The large difference between the HOW and the HOC can be a result of an excessively long suction line or missing, loose, damaged or improperly installed suction line insulation.

Side note:

Properly insulating the suction line, will cause the whole compressor line (from point "D" to point "E" to move to the left, lowering the HOC.

63

PRESSURE ENTHALPY: SYSTEM CHARACTERISTICS

The Mysterious 42.42

As part of a number of pressure enthalpy-related calculations, there is a conversion factor that shows up time and time again. For the sake of completeness, a brief explanation of where this conversion factor comes from is in order.

When dealing with air conditioning and refrigeration systems, we often face the issues of system power consumption and motor horsepower. Horsepower is a measure of work done per unit time. For example, if a 33-pound object was moved 1,000 feet, it is said that 33,000 foot-pounds of work has been done. The formula for work is:

WORK = Weight of an object in pounds x Distance moved

From this formula we can verify that moving our 33-pound object 1,000 feet will result in 33,000 foot-pounds of work having been done. In a similar manner, we can confirm that moving a 66-pound object 500 feet will result in the same 33,000 foot-pounds of work. We can also say that moving a 1-pound object 33,000 feet results in the same amount of work being done, Figure 56.

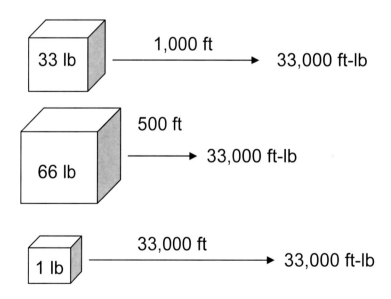

Figure 56. Various combinations of weight and distance require the same amount of work.

Notice how the units of work, ft-lb, do not take into account the amount of time it takes to move a particular weight a certain distance. When we add a time variable into the mix, we get power, or horsepower. We say that when 33,000 ft-lb of work is done in a time period of 1 minute, 1 horsepower of work has been done. Therefore:

$$1 \text{ Hp} = 33,000 \text{ ft-lb/min}$$

Example #28:

Consider the situation where 66,000 ft-lb of work is done in 4 minutes. Calculate the horsepower for this scenario.

Solution:

The total amount of work done is 66,000 ft-lb over a period of 4 minutes. This equates to 66,000 ft-lb ÷ 4 minutes = 16,500 ft-lb/min.

Since 1 horsepower is equal to 33,000 ft-lb/min, 16,500 ft-lb/min is equal to 0.5 horsepower as shown here:

Hp = [Work/time in minutes] ÷ 33,000 ft-lb/min
Hp = [66,000 ft-lb/4 minutes] ÷ 33,000 ft-lb/min
Hp = 16,500 ft-lb/min ÷ 33,000 ft-lb/min
Hp = 0.5

Having got this far, we now need to convert the units of ft-lb into heat, or btu. It takes 778 ft-lb of work to generate 1 btu of heat energy. So, if we divide this value into our 33,000 ft-lb/min, we get:

$$[33,000 \text{ ft-lb/min}] ÷ [778 \text{ ft-lb/btu}] = 42.42 \text{ btu/min-Hp}$$

Side note:

The good news is that it is highly unlikely that you will ever have to derive this conversion factor again, but it's always nice to know where it came from!

PRESSURE ENTHALPY: SYSTEM CHARACTERISTICS

Theoretical Horsepower per Ton (THp/Ton)

Every air conditioning and refrigeration system is equipped with a compressor that is likely rated in horsepower. Just as with any motor, the horsepower rating determines the amount of work that the motor can do per unit time. Refer back to the previous section on the mysterious 42.42 for more on the concept of work and work per unit time.

The theoretical horsepower per ton, THp/Ton, tells us how many horsepower are required under the present system conditions to produce one ton of refrigeration. For example, if we have a 10 horsepower motor in our compressor and the THp/Ton is 0.5, that means that for every 0.5 horsepower we have available, we can obtain one ton of refrigeration. In this case, we can get 20 tons of refrigeration since $10 \div 0.5 = 20$.

If we had the same 10 horsepower compressor motor and our THp/Ton was equal to 2, we would be able to obtain 5 tons of refrigeration, since $10 \div 2 = 5$.

In order to determine the THp/Ton, we use the mass flow rate per ton as well as the heat of work and our 42.42 constant to get:

Theoretical Horsepower per Ton, THp/ton = (MFR/ton x HOW) ÷ 42.42

Refer back to pages 53 though 56 for a quick review of MFR/ton and HOW if needed.

Example #29:

Consider the system in Figure 57. Calculate the following:

- NRE
- MFR/Ton
- HOW
- HOC
- COP
- THp/Ton

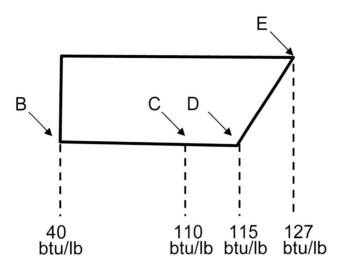

Figure 57. Example #29.

Solution:

NRE = Heat Content at Point "C" – Heat Content at Point "B"
NRE = 110 btu/lb - 40 btu/lb
NRE = 70 btu/lb

MFR/Ton = 200 ÷ NRE
MFR/Ton = 200 ÷ 70 btu/lb
MFR/Ton = 2.86 lb/min/Ton

HOW = Heat Content at Point "E" – Heat Content at Point "D"
HOW = 127 btu/lb - 115 btu/lb
HOW = 12 btu/lb

HOC = Heat Content at Point "E" – Heat Content at Point "C"
HOC = 127 btu/lb - 110 btu/lb
HOC = 17 btu/lb

Coefficient of Performance, COP = NRE ÷ HOC
Coefficient of Performance, COP = 70 btu/lb ÷ 17 btu/lb
Coefficient of Performance, COP = 4.1

THp/Ton = (MFR/ton x HOW) ÷ 42.42
THp/Ton = (2.86 lb/min/Ton x 12 btu/lb) ÷ 42.42 btu/min-Hp
THp/Ton = 34.32 btu/min ÷ 42.42 btu/min-Hp
THp/Ton = 0.81

So, if we had a 10 horsepower motor in our compressor, the system capacity would be about 12.35 tons, since 10 Hp ÷ 0.81 Hp/Ton = 12.35 Tons.

PRESSURE ENTHALPY: SYSTEM CHARACTERISTICS

Total Heat of Rejection (THOR)

At the beginning of this book we mentioned that the basic vapor-compression refrigeration cycle is a repeating cycle. Everything that was done had to be undone later on to ensure that the system was back exactly where it began in preparation to begin another cycle. As part of this process, any heat that is absorbed into the system must later be rejected. If such is not the case and the heat is not rejected, heat will accumulate in the system and eventually cause the system to fail. The amount of heat that must be rejected is, therefore, the total amount of all heat generated and absorbed into the system. This heat can be attributed to these sources:

- Latent heat absorbed by the evaporator from the medium being cooled
- Sensible heat absorbed by the evaporator from the medium being cooled
- Sensible heat picked up in the suction line from the air surrounding the lines
- Sensible heat picked up in the compressor as a result of the compression process
- Sensible heat resulting from the friction of the compressor's internal moving parts

The first two items on the above list represent our NRE, or the cooling effect that is taking place in the evaporator. The third item on the list is our suction line. The last two items on the list take place in our compressor and are represented by the HOW.

Combining the suction line (point "C" to "D" on the pressure enthalpy chart) with our HOW (between points "D" and "E" on the pressure enthalpy chart), we get our HOC.

Our Total Heat of Rejection, THOR, is therefore equal to the NRE plus the HOC.

The system begins rejecting heat as soon as the refrigerant is discharged from the compressor and continues to reject heat until the refrigerant enters the metering device. So, system heat is rejected by the discharge line, the condenser as well as the liquid line. Refrigerant leaves the compressor at point "E" and enters the metering device at point "A", Figure 58 so,

Total Heat of Rejection, THOR = Heat Content at Point "E" – Heat Content at Point "A"

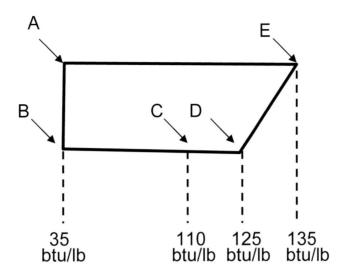

Figure 58. The Total Heat of Rejection is calculated between points "E" and "A".

Example #30:

From the information in Figure 58, calculate the THOR three ways. Use the direct formula, the NRE + HOC method and the NRE + HOW + Suction line method. Verify that they all produce the same result.

Solution:

THOR = Heat Content at Point "E" – Heat Content at Point "A"
THOR = 135 btu/lb – 35 btu/lb
THOR = 100 btu/lb

THOR = NRE + HOC
THOR = [110 btu/lb – 35 btu/lb] + [135 btu/lb – 110 btu/lb]
THOR = 75 btu/lb + 25 btu/lb
THOR = 100 btu/lb

THOR = NRE + HOW + Suction Line
THOR = [110 btu/lb – 35 btu/lb] + [135 btu/lb – 125 btu/lb] + Suction Line
THOR = 75 btu/lb + 10 btu/lb + Suction Line
THOR = 85 btu/lb + [125 btu/lb – 110 btu/lb]
THOR = 85 btu/lb + 15 btu/lb
THOR = 100 btu/lb

PRESSURE ENTHALPY: SYSTEM CHARACTERISTICS

Mass Flow Rate of the System (MFR/System)

Earlier in this portion of the book we discussed the Mass Flow Rate per Ton (pages 53 and 54). This system parameter was directly related to the NRE and told us how much refrigerant needed to circulate through the system in order to produce one ton of refrigeration. The difference between the MFR/ton and the MFR/system is that the MFR/ton provides the flow for each ton of refrigeration, while the MFR/system provides us with the total amount of refrigerant flowing through our specific system.

For example, consider a system that is providing exactly 5 tons of cooling and has a MFR/ton of 2 lb/min/ton. This means that for every ton of cooling the system must circulate 2 pounds of refrigerant past any given point in the system every minute. So, since the system is providing 5 tons of cooling, the MFR/system must be five times the MFR/ton, or 10 lb/min.

Since we cannot determine the exact capacity of the system yet, we use this formula to determine the Mass Flow Rate of the system:

$$MFR/system = [42.42 \, (Hp)] \div HOW$$

Example #31:

  Using the system in Figure 58, determine the MFR/system if the compressor motor is sized at 5 horsepower.

Solution:

  From example #30, we can determine that the HOW is equal to 10 btu/lb.

  Using the above formula, we get:

  MFR/system = [42.42 (Hp)] ÷ HOW
  MFR/system = [42.42 (5)] ÷ 10 btu/lb
  MFR/system = 212.1 ÷ 10 btu/lb
  MFR/system = 21.21 lb/min

Example #32:

  Using the information from Figure 58 and the answer from example #31, calculate the system's cooling capacity in tons.

Solution:

We can determine the system capacity a number of different ways using the information we have covered so far, so we will solve this example two different ways.

METHOD #1

We will use the MFR/system and the MFR/ton to determine the system capacity. The MFR/ton is found by:

MFR/ton = 200 ÷ NRE
MFR/ton = 200 ÷ [110btu/lb – 35 btu/lb]
MFR/ton = 200 ÷ 75 btu/lb
MFR/ton = 2.67 lb/min/ton

Since the MFR/system is 21.21 lb/min (from example #31) and the MFR/ton is 2.6, we can determine the system's cooling capacity by:

Cooling capacity (in tons) = MFR/system ÷ MFR/ton
Cooling capacity (in tons) = 21.21 lb/min ÷ 2.67 lb/min/ton
Cooling capacity (in tons) = 7.94 tons

METHOD #2

Secondly, since we know that we have a 5 horsepower motor, we can use the THp/ton to determine the system's cooling capacity:

THp/Ton = (MFR/ton x HOW) ÷ 42.42
THp/Ton = (2.67 lb/min/ton x 10 btu/lb) ÷ 42.42
THp/ton = 0.629 HP/ton

Since the compressor motor is 5 Hp, we can determine the cooling capacity of the system as follows:

Cooling capacity (in tons) = Motor Hp ÷ THp/ton
Cooling capacity (in tons) = 5 Hp ÷ 0.629 Hp/ton
Cooling capacity (in tons) = 7.95 tons

In case you would like a third way to calculate system capacity, turn the page.

PRESSURE ENTHALPY: SYSTEM CHARACTERISTICS

Evaporator Capacity (CAP/evap)

Just in case the two previous methods (page 71) weren't enough for you, here is another formula that you can use to determine the capacity of the system evaporator:

Capacity of the Evaporator = MFR/system (lb/min) x NRE (btu/lb) x 60 (min/hour)

MFR/system is given in lb/min, NRE is given in btu/lb and 60 is the conversion between minutes and hours and is given in min/hour. When multiplied together, the units become

lb/min x btu/lb x min/hour = btu/hour

Once the evaporator capacity has been determined in btu/hour, we can then determine the tonnage of the evaporator by dividing the evaporator capacity in btu/hour by 12,000 btu/hour/ton. This will give us the number of tons of capacity at which the evaporator is operating. The formula looks like this:

Evaporator Tonnage = Evaporator Capacity in btu/hr ÷ 12,000 btu/hr/ton

Example #33:

Using the information from examples 31 and 32, use the above formula to determine the system capacity in btu/hour and tons.

Solution:

Using the formula for evaporator capacity in btu/hour, we get:

CAP/evap = MFR/system (lb/min) x NRE (btu/lb) x 60 (min/hour)

CAP/evap = 21.21 lb/min x 75 btu/lb x 60 min/hour

CAP/evap = 95,445 btu/hour

To convert this capacity to tons we use the following:

Evaporator Tonnage = Evaporator Capacity in btu/hr ÷ 12,000 btu/hr/ton

Evaporator Tonnage = 95,445 btu/hr ÷ 12,000 btu/hr/ton

Evaporator Tonnage = 7.95 tons

Side note:

Compare the results from the two methods used on page 71 with the results just obtained here. All three methods yield the exact same results!

You know what the system nameplate says, but how can you be sure that's what the system is actually putting out?

So now, with a few temperature and pressure measurements, you will be able to determine the capacity of the system you are working on at that point in time.

How professional would it be to present your customers with written reports containing vital system information such as this?

But the fun isn't over yet.

PRESSURE ENTHALPY: SYSTEM CHARACTERISTICS

Condenser Capacity (CAP/cond)

Just as the evaporator capacity can be calculated in terms of btu/hour and tons, we can also determine the capacity of the condenser. The capacity of the condenser is the number of btu/hour that are rejected by the system. The system begins to reject heat the moment the hot gas is discharged from the compressor and continues until the refrigerant enters the metering device. The formula for the condenser capacity is given by:

Capacity of the Condenser = MFR/system (lb/min) x THOR (btu/lb) x 60 (min/hour)

MFR/system is given in lb/min, THOR is given in btu/lb and 60 is the conversion between minutes and hours and minutes and is given in min/hour. When multiplied together, the units become

lb/min x btu/lb x min/hour = btu/hour

Once the condenser capacity has been determined in btu/hour, we can then determine the tonnage of the condenser by dividing the condenser capacity in btu/hour by 12,000 btu/hour/ton to obtain the number of tons of capacity at which the condenser is operating. The formula looks like this:

Condenser Tonnage = Condenser Capacity in btu/hr ÷ 12,000 btu/hr/ton

Side note:

> The condenser tonnage should always be larger than the evaporator tonnage. This is because the MFR/system and the 60 min/hour portions of these calculations are the same, but the THOR is larger than the NRE. The condenser must reject more heat than the evaporator absorbs since the condenser must also reject heat introduced to the system from the suction line and during the compression process.

Example #34:

From the information provided in Figure 59, calculate the NRE, HOW, HOC, COP, THOR, MFR/system and the CAP/cond if the compressor has a 5 horsepower motor.

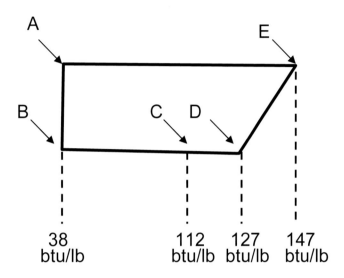

Figure 59. Example #34.

Solution:

NRE = Heat Content at Point "C" – Heat Content at Point "B"
NRE = 112 btu/lb - 38 btu/lb
NRE = 74 btu/lb

HOW = Heat Content at Point "E" – Heat Content at Point "D"
HOW = 147 btu/lb - 127 btu/lb
HOW = 20 btu/lb

HOC = Heat Content at Point "E" – Heat Content at Point "C"
HOC = 147 btu/lb - 112 btu/lb
HOC = 35 btu/lb

COP = NRE ÷ HOC
COP = 74 btu/lb ÷ 35 btu/lb
COP = 2.1

THOR = Heat Content at Point "E" – Heat Content at Point "A"
THOR = 147 btu/lb - 38 btu/lb
THOR = 109 btu/lb

MFR/system = [42.42 (Hp)] ÷ HOW
MFR/system = [42.42 (5)] ÷ 20 btu/lb
MFR/system = 212.1 ÷ 20 btu/lb
MFR/system = 10.6 lb/min

CAP/cond = MFR/system (lb/min) x THOR (btu/lb) x 60 (min/hour)
CAP/cond = 10.6 lb/min x 109 btu/lb x 60 min/hour
CAP/cond = 69,324 btu/hour

Condenser Tonnage = Condenser Capacity in btu/hr ÷ 12,000 btu/hr/ton
Condenser Tonnage = 69,324 btu/hr ÷ 12,000 btu/hr/ton
Condenser Tonnage = 5.8 tons

PRESSURE ENTHALPY: SYSTEM CHARACTERISTICS

Compressor Capacity (CAP/comp)

The capacity of the compressor provides the volume of refrigerant, in cubic feet, that are circulated through the system per minute. To accomplish this calculation we use the mass flow rate of the system, which gives us the number of pounds of refrigerant circulated every minute and the specific volume, which provides a relationship between the number of cubic feet of refrigerant that are needed to make up each pound of refrigerant. The specific volume of the refrigerant is measured at the inlet of the compressor, which is point "D" on the pressure enthalpy chart, Figure 60.

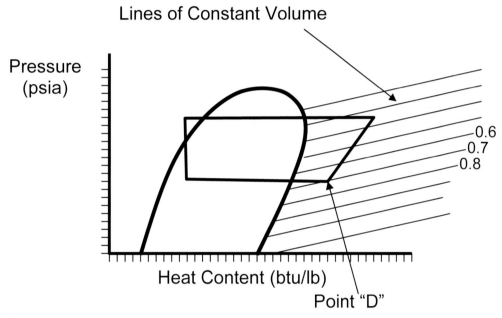

Figure 60. The specific volume of the refrigerant is measured at the inlet of the compressor at Point "D" on the pressure enthalpy chart.

The value of the specific volume is read from the scale at the right side of the chart. The formula for the compressor capacity is:

Capacity of the Compressor = MFR/system x Specific Volume

Example #35:

Consider the pressure enthalpy plot in Figure 60. Calculate the compressor capacity in cubic feet per minute (cfm) if the MFR/system is equal to 25 lb/min.

Solution:

Capacity of the Compressor = MFR/system x Specific Volume
Capacity of the Compressor = 25 lb/min x 0.7 ft^3/lb = 17.5 cfm

PRESSURE ENTHALPY: SYSTEM CHARACTERISTICS

Energy Efficiency Ratio (EER)

Back on pages 62 and 63 we discussed the coefficient of performance, COP, of the system, which gave us an indication of the efficiency of the system. To calculate the COP we divided the NRE by the HOC to obtain a unitless result, which compared our cooling effect, removal of heat, to the amount of heat added to the system.

The energy efficiency ratio, EER, however, is not a unitless parameter. The EER is a system rating that compares the cooling output, in btu, to the power input in watts. Once we have calculated the COP, it is an easy task to determine the EER of the system by using the following formula:

$$EER = COP \times 3.413$$

The 3.413 is the conversion factor between btu and watts, as 3.413 btu = 1 watt of power. The above formula can also be presented as:

$$COP = EER \times 0.293$$

Both of the above equations are exactly the same. The first formula, however, is more useful for us as service technicians as we would like to determine the EER and then compare this value to the nameplate to evaluate system performance.

Example #36:

    Using the information from Example #34, calculate the EER for the system.

Solution:

    From Example #34, we determined that the NRE = 74 btu/lb, the HOC = 35 btu/lb and the COP = 2.11. The COP was found by dividing the NRE by the HOC.

    Using the EER formula:

    EER = COP x 3.413
    EER = 2.11 x 3.413
    EER = 7.2

    For the most part, the EER for this system is too low and not acceptable. This could have been predicted, given the large HOC compared to the NRE. Notice from the Example #34 information and calculations, the HOW is 20 btu/lb and the HOC is 35 btu/lb.

Example #37:

  After evaluating the system in Example #36, it was found that a large portion of the suction line insulation was missing. The service technician replaced the insulation and properly sealed the mating surfaces of the insulation. The NRE remained the same at 74 btu/lb, but the HOC dropped to 23 btu/lb. Calculate the new EER.

Solution:

  First, we need to calculate the COP:

  COP = NRE ÷ HOC
  COP = 74 btu/lb ÷ 23 btu/lb
  COP = 3.22

  Using the EER formula:

  EER = COP x 3.413
  EER = 3.22 x 3.413
  EER = 10.99

Side note:

  The EER rating is typically used for unitary units, not for split-type central systems and heat pumps. However, the EER does provide a useful base on which we can evaluate other systems.

PRESSURE ENTHALPY: SYSTEM CHARACTERISTICS

Seasonal Energy Efficiency Ratio (SEER)

The seasonal energy efficiency ratio, SEER, is an extension of the EER discussed before. The main difference between the two is that the EER value can be inaccurate as the system performance changes with the outdoor ambient temperature. The SEER is intended to be an evaluation of the system over an entire cooling season, so it compensates for the varying operating conditions under which the system operates.

The tests that are used to establish the SEER are complex and are performed by independent parties. The tests involve operating the system under a number of conditions including

- Periods of very high humidity
- Periods of very low humidity
- Timed on and off cycles such as 6 minutes on and 24 minutes off for an extended period of time

Since most air conditioning systems are designed to operate at their rated capacities when the outside ambient temperature is 95°F, systems become more and more efficient as the outside temperature falls. Since systems only operate at design conditions for a fraction of the cooling year, the SEER rating is typically higher than the EER rating.

As system performance varies depending on the geographic location of the system, so does the SEER rating. For this reason, we will provide a means to calculate a SEER range within which most systems will fall. This SEER rating range is directly related to the EER rating that we calculated in the previous section.

The following two equations will provide a workable range of SEER ratings:

$$\text{SEER (lower end)} = 1.1 \times \text{EER}$$

$$\text{SEER (higher end)} = 1.3 \times \text{EER}$$

Example #38:

There is an air conditioning system that is operating an NRE of 70 btu/lb and a HOC of 20 btu/lb. Calculate the COP, EER and range of SEER for this system.

Solution:

COP = NRE ÷ HOC
COP = 70 btu/lb ÷ 20 btu/lb
COP = 3.5

EER = COP x 3.413
EER = 3.5 x 3.413
EER = 11.95

SEER (low end) = 1.1 x EER
SEER (low end) = 1.1 x 11.95
SEER (low end) = 13.1

SEER (high end) = 1.3 x EER
SEER (high end) = 1.3 x 11.95
SEER (high end) = 15.5

Side note:

Given the new 13 SEER requirements that took effect in January, 2006, it can be seen from the previous example that the COP for new systems should be in the 3.5 range. A COP of 3.5 will provide us with a SEER rating that falls between 13.1 and 15.5.

PRESSURE ENTHALPY: PLOTTING THE SYSTEM

Having discussed the layout of the pressure enthalpy chart and all of the system parameters that we can calculate from a successfully plotted system, we are now ready to start putting the system to paper.

The pages that follow provide step-by-step procedures to prepare a graphic representation of the system you are working on.

SYSTEM #1: Normal Operating Conditions (high temperature application)

Consider an R-22 air conditioning system operating with the following conditions:

Condenser Saturation Pressure: 278 psig
Evaporator Saturation Pressure: 68.5 psig
Evaporator Outlet Temperature: 50°F
Condenser Outlet Temperature: 100°F
Compressor Discharge Temperature: 180°F
System utilizes R-22 and has a 5 Horsepower reciprocating compressor

Plot the following system on a pressure enthalpy diagram and calculate these system parameters:

Compression Ratio	COP	CAP/cond
NRE	MFR/ton	CAP/comp
HOW	THp/ton	EER
HOC	MFR/system	SEER range
THOR	CAP/evap	

Step 1: Convert the saturation pressures from gauge pressures to absolute pressures.

        Condenser Saturation Pressure: 278 psig + 14.7 = 292.7 psia
        Condenser Saturation Pressure = 293 psia

        Evaporator Saturation Pressure: 68.5 psig + 14.7 = 83.2 psia
        Evaporator Saturation Pressure = 83 psia

Step 2: Draw the pressure lines on the pressure enthalpy chart.

        Draw horizontal lines across the pressure enthalpy chart at the corresponding absolute pressures. These lines represent the high and low pressure sides of the system. Use the scales on both sides of the chart to ensure accurately drawn lines, Figure 61.

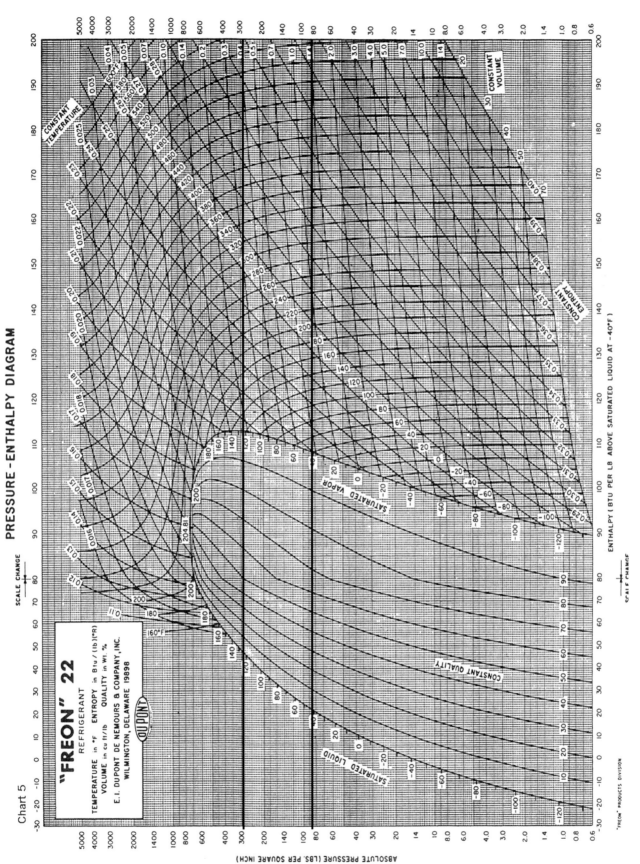

Figure 61. High and low pressure lines drawn across the pressure enthalpy diagram at the corresponding system absolute pressures. Pressure enthalpy chart courtesy DuPont.

83

Step 3: Locate the compressor discharge temperature.

You will locate the compressor discharge temperature on the constant temperature lines. The point where this line crosses the high pressure line represents the point at which the refrigerant leaves the compressor. This point is labeled "E", Figure 62. In our example, the compressor discharge temperature is 180°F. *See side note if your compressor is a hermetically sealed, low side dome compressor.*

Side note:

If the compressor in the system you are working on is a hermetically sealed, low side dome compressor, the compressor discharge temperature measurement will be lower than the actual temperature at the outlet of the compressor. This is because the compressor itself is located within the shell of the device and the discharge gas must first pass through this low pressure, low temperature space before exiting the shell of the component. If this is the case, follow steps 4 and 4a instead of 3 and 3a.

Step 3a: Draw the compressor line.

From point "E", follow a line of constant entropy down until this line crosses the low pressure line. This point represents the inlet of the compressor and is referred to as point "D", Figure 62.

Skip to Step #5.

Step 4: Locate the compressor inlet temperature.

(For hermetically sealed, low side dome compressors)

Take a temperature reading at the inlet of the compressor, approximately four to six inches from the compressor on the suction line. You will locate the compressor inlet temperature on the constant temperature lines. The point where this line crosses the low pressure line represents the point at which the refrigerant enters the compressor. This point is labeled "D". For this example, we will use 70°F as the compressor inlet temperature, Figure 62.

Step 4a: Draw the compressor line.

(For hermetically sealed, low side dome compressors)

From point "D", follow a line of constant entropy up until this line crosses the high pressure line. This point represents the outlet of the compressor and is referred to as point "E", Figure 62.

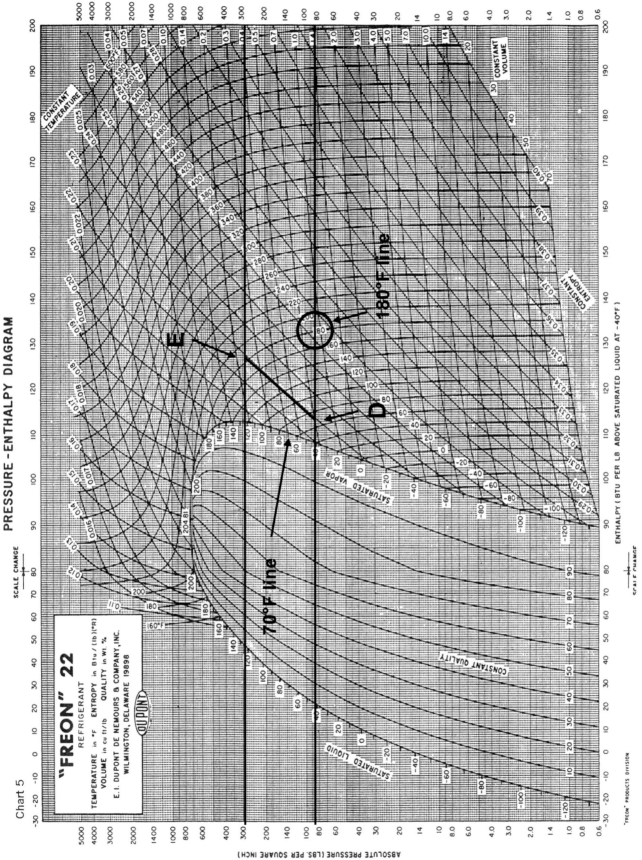

Figure 62. The compressor line on the pressure enthalpy chart. Pressure enthalpy chart courtesy DuPont.

85

Step 5: Locate the condenser outlet temperature.

The condenser outlet temperature (100°F in this example) is found on the left side of the saturation curve. Draw a vertical line through this point. The point where this line crosses the high pressure line represents the point where the liquid refrigerant leaves the condenser. This point is referred to as point "A". The point where this line crosses the low pressure line represents the point where the refrigerant enters the evaporator. This point is referred to as point "B", Figure 63.

Side note:

This vertical line represents an adiabatic process. This type of process is one in which the temperature and pressure of the refrigerant are reduced, but the heat content, enthalpy in btu/lb, remains the same. This can be seen by the fact that as we move from point "A" to point "B", the line cuts through both the lines of constant pressure and the lines of constant temperature. The line connecting points "A" and "B", however, remains parallel to the lines of constant enthalpy.

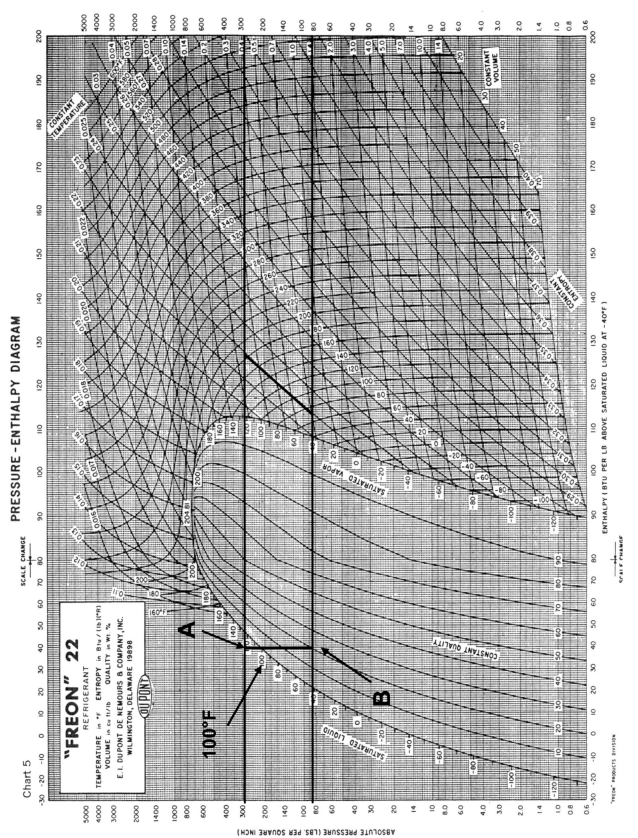

Figure 63. The adiabatic process between points "A" and "B" represents the metering device. Pressure enthalpy chart courtesy DuPont.

87

Step 6: Locate the evaporator outlet temperature.

The evaporator outlet temperature is found on the right side of the saturation curve. Follow the 50°F line of constant temperature down until the line crosses the low pressure line. This point represents the outlet evaporator and is referred to as point "C", Figure 64.

The evaporator of the system is located between points "B" and "C" on the pressure enthalpy chart.

Step 7: Draw vertical lines and obtain enthalpy readings.

Drawing vertical lines through points A, B, C, D and E will give heat content (enthalpy) readings at either the top or bottom of the chart. Make note of these values as they are used for the following calculations, Figure 64. The values obtained for our example should be very close to the following:

Heat content at point "A": 39 btu/lb
Heat content at point "B": 39 btu/lb
Heat content at point "C": 109 btu/lb
Heat content at point "D": 113 btu/lb
Heat content at point "E": 127 btu/lb

Side note:

Notice that the heat content at point "A" is the same as the heat content at point "B". This is because of the adiabatic process where the heat content remains the same, while the temperature and pressure of the refrigerant change.

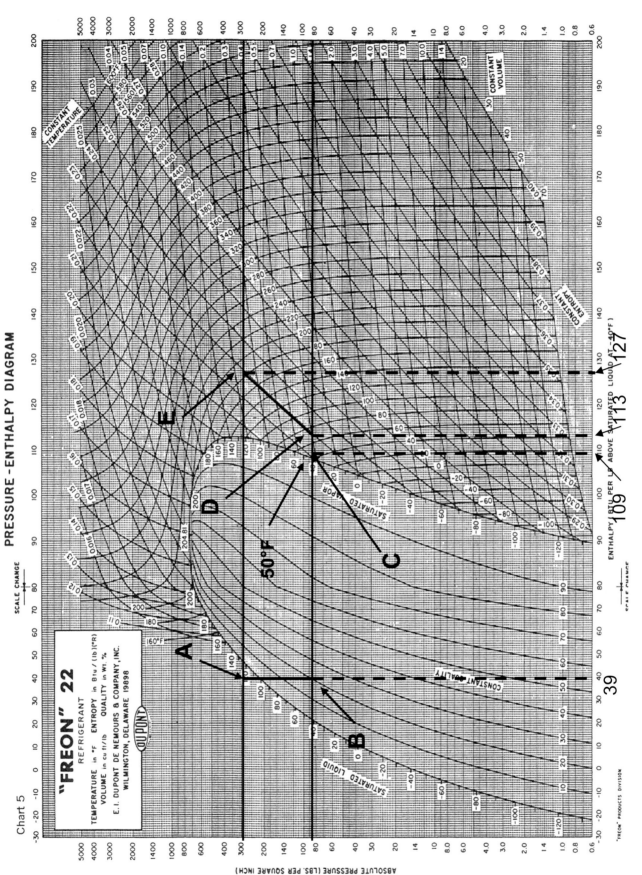

Figure 64. The evaporator outlet at point "C". Heat content values at points "A" through "E" labeled. Pressure enthalpy chart courtesy DuPont.

Step 8: Obtain the specific volume reading.

The specific volume of the refrigerant is measured at the inlet of the compressor, point "D" on the chart, Figure 65. For this particular system, this value is about 0.7 ft³/lb.

Step 9: Perform the calculations.(Take a deep breath)

Step 9a: Compression Ratio

Compression Ratio= High Side (psia) ÷ Low Side (psia)
Compression Ratio = 293 psia ÷ 83 psia (*refer back to Step#1 for calculations*)
Compression Ratio = 3.53:1

Step 9b: Net Refrigeration Effect, NRE

Net Refrigeration Effect, NRE = C – B (*refer to Step 7 for enthalpy values*)
NRE = 109 btu/lb – 39 btu/lb
NRE = 70 btu/lb

Step 9c: Heat of Compression, HOC

Heat of Compression, HOC = E – C (*refer to Step 7 for enthalpy values*)
HOC = 127 btu/lb – 109 btu/lb
HOC = 18 btu/lb

Step 9d: Heat of Work, HOW

Heat of Work, HOW = E – D (*refer to Step 7 for enthalpy values*)
HOW = 127 btu/lb – 113 btu/lb
HOW = 14 btu/lb

Step 9e: Total Heat of Rejection, THOR

Total Heat of Rejection, THOR = E – A (*refer to Step 7 for enthalpy values*)
THOR = 127 btu/lb – 39 btu/lb
THOR = 88 btu/lb

Step 9f: Coefficient of Performance, COP

Coefficient of Performance, COP = NRE ÷ HOC (*Steps 9b and 9c*)
COP = 70 btu/lb ÷ 18 btu/lb
COP = 3.9

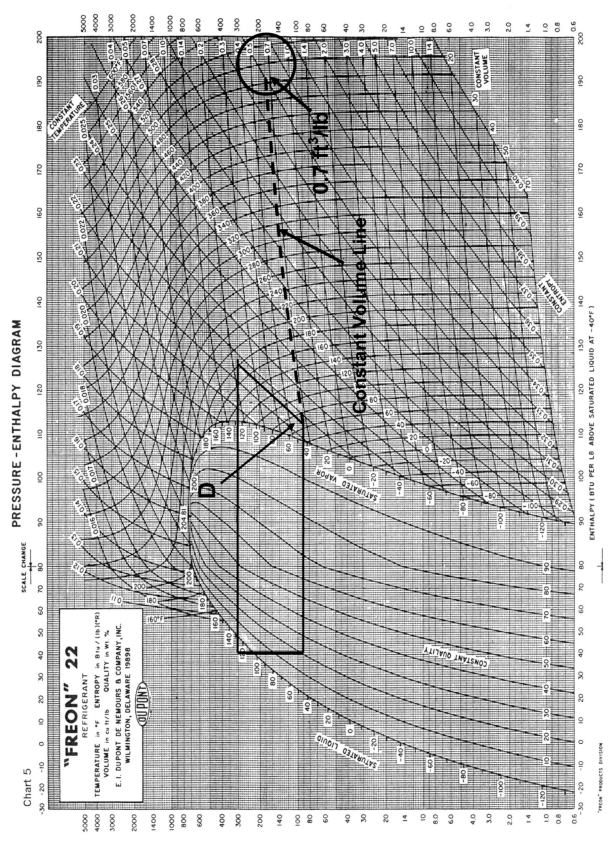

Figure 65. The specific volume is measured at the inlet of the compressor at point "D". Pressure enthalpy chart courtesy DuPont.

Step 9g: Mass Flow Rate per Ton, MFR/ton

Mass Flow Rate per Ton, MFR/ton = 200 ÷ NRE
MFR/ton = 200 ÷ 70 btu/lb
MFR/ton = 2.86 lb/min/ton

Step 9h: Theoretical HP per ton, THp/ton

Theoretical HP per ton, THp/ton = (MFR/ton x HOW) ÷ 42.42
THp/ton = (2.86 lb/min/ton x 14 btu/lb) ÷ 42.42
THp/ton = 0.94 Hp/ton

Step 9i: Mass Flow Rate/System, MFR/system

Mass Flow Rate/System, MFR/system = 42.42 x Hp ÷ HOW
MFR/system = 42.42 x 5 ÷ HOW
MFR/system = 212.10 ÷ 14 btu/lb
MFR/system = 15.15 lb/min

Step 9j: Capacity of the Evaporator, btu/hour

Capacity of the Evaporator = MFR/system x NRE x 60
Capacity/evaporator = 15.15 lb/min x 70 btu/lb x 60 min/hour
Capacity/evaporator = 63,630 btu/hour

Step 9k: Capacity of the Evaporator, tons

Evaporator Tonnage = 63,630 btu/hour ÷ 12,000 btu/hour/ton
Evaporator Tonnage = 5.3 tons

Step 9l: *Capacity of the Condenser, btu/hour*

Capacity of the Condenser = MFR/system x THOR x 60
Capacity/condenser = 15.15 lb/min x 88 btu/lb x 60 min/hour
Capacity/condenser = 79,992 btu/hour

Step 9m: *Capacity of the Condenser, tons*

Condenser Tonnage = 79,992 btu/hour ÷ 12,000 btu/hour/ton
Condenser Tonnage = 6.67 tons

Step 9n: Capacity of the Compressor

Capacity of the Compressor = MFR/system x Specific Volume
Capacity/compressor = 15.15 lb/min x 0.7 ft³/lb (*refer to step #8*)
Capacity/compressor = 10.6 ft³/min

Step 9o: Energy Efficiency Ratio, EER

Energy Efficiency Ratio, EER = COP x 3.413
Energy Efficiency Ratio, EER = 3.9 x 3.413 (*refer to step 9f for COP*)
Energy Efficiency Ratio, EER = 13.3

Step 9p: Seasonal Energy Efficiency Ratio, SEER – Low end of the range

Seasonal Energy Efficiency Ratio, SEER (low end) = 1.1 x EER
SEER (low end) = 1.1 x 13.3
SEER (low end) = 14.63

Step 9q: Seasonal Energy Efficiency Ratio, SEER – High end of the range

Seasonal Energy Efficiency Ratio, SEER (high end) = 1.3 x EER
SEER (high end) = 1.3 x 13.3
SEER (high end) = 17.3

SYSTEM #2: Normal Operating Conditions (medium temperature application)

This is a system that is operating properly but, instead of providing the operating pressures as in the previous example, the data provided are strictly temperatures, along with the compressor motor size, which is 5 horsepower. The system information is as follows:

Condenser saturation temperature: 120°F
Condenser outlet temperature: 100°F
Evaporator saturation temperature: 20°F
Evaporator outlet temperature: 40°F
Compressor inlet temperature: 60°F
Compressor horsepower: 5 Hp
System refrigerant: R-134a

As in the previous example, we will compute the following system parameters:

Compression Ratio	COP	CAP/cond
NRE	MFR/ton	CAP/comp
HOW	THp/ton	EER
HOC	MFR/system	SEER range
THOR	CAP/evap	

Side note:

> Since the system information already provides us with the condenser and evaporator saturation temperatures, there is no need to use the pressure/temperature chart to convert pressures to temperatures. The condenser and evaporator saturation temperatures are given as 120°F and 20°F respectively.

Step 1: Draw the pressure lines on the pressure enthalpy chart.

> Draw horizontal lines across the pressure enthalpy chart at the corresponding saturation temperatures, Figure 66. These lines, as before, represent the high and low pressure sides of the system.

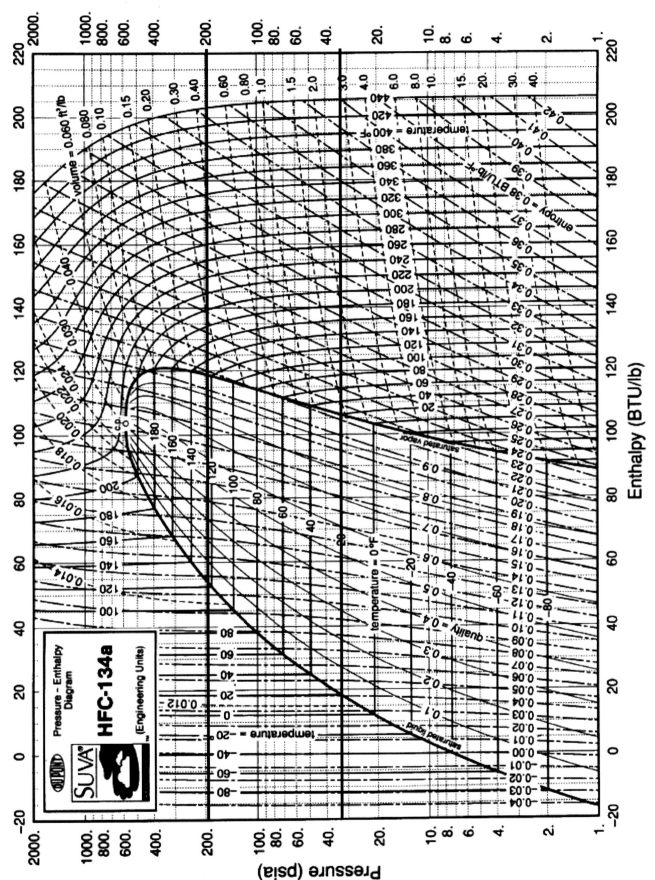

Figure 66. The high and low side pressure lines correspond to the saturation temperatures of 120°F and 20°F, respectively. Pressure enthalpy chart courtesy DuPont.

95

Step 2: Draw the compressor line.

In this example, the temperature at the inlet of the compressor is given as 60°F. Locate 60°F constant temperature line on the right side of the saturation curve. The point where this line crosses the low side pressure line is point "D", which is the inlet of the compressor, Figure 67.

From point "D", follow a line of constant entropy up until this line crosses the high pressure line, Figure 67. This point is the outlet of the system compressor.

From Figure 67, we can also see that the temperature at the outlet of the compressor is about 170°F.

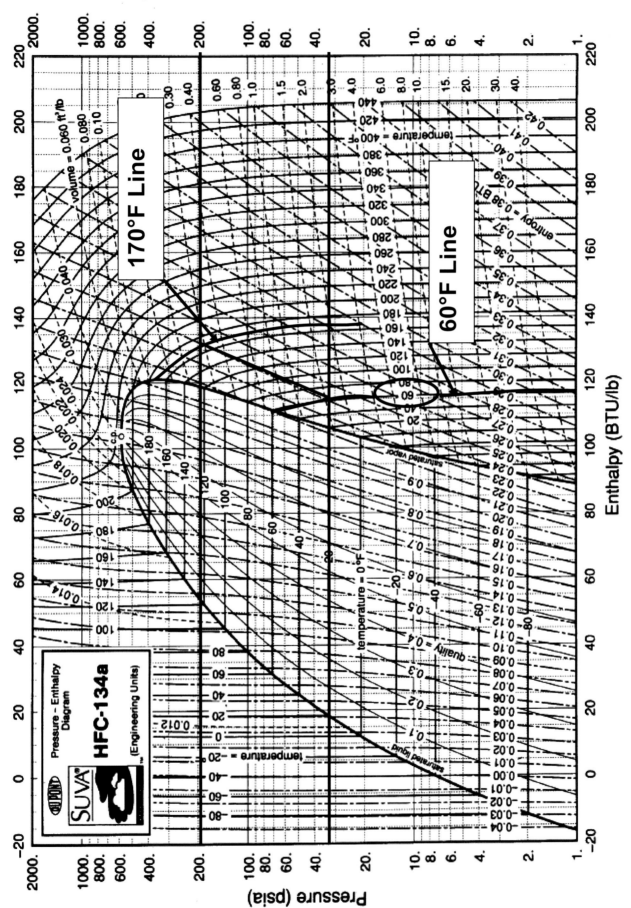

Figure 67. The compressor line represents the compressor inlet temperature of 60°F and an outlet temperature of 170°F. Pressure enthalpy chart courtesy DuPont.

97

Step 3: Draw the metering device line.

Locate the condenser outlet temperature (100°F) on the left side of the saturation curve. Draw a vertical line through this point, Figure 68. The point where this line crosses the high pressure line represents the point where the liquid refrigerant leaves the condenser. This point is referred to as point "A". The point where this line crosses the low pressure line represents the point where the refrigerant enters the evaporator. This point is referred to as point "B".

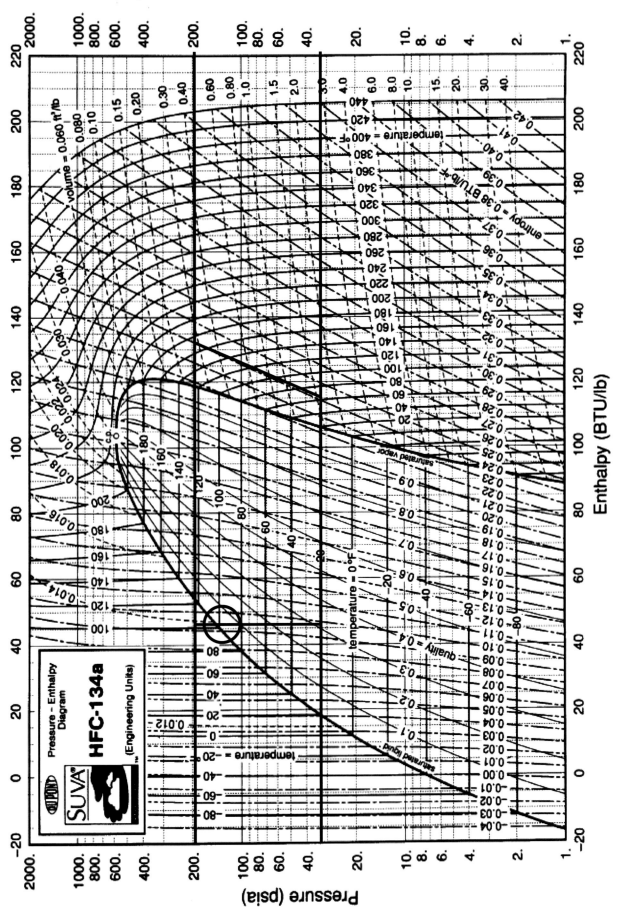

Figure 68. The condenser outlet temperature of 100°F is the point through which our metering device line passes. Pressure enthalpy chart courtesy DuPont.

66

Step 4: Locate the evaporator outlet.

Point "C", the evaporator outlet is found by first locating the 40°F constant temperature line on the right side of the saturation curve. Then, locate the point where this line crosses the low pressure line, Figure 69. This point is the evaporator outlet.

Step 5: Identify enthalpy points.

Drawing vertical lines through points A, B, C, D and E will give heat content (enthalpy) readings at either the top or bottom of the chart, Figure 70. Make note of these values as they are used for the following calculations. The obtained values should be very close to the following:

Heat content at point "A": 46 btu/lb
Heat content at point "B": 46 btu/lb
Heat content at point "C": 110 btu/lb
Heat content at point "D": 115 btu/lb
Heat content at point "E": 132 btu/lb

The completed plot will look similar to that in Figure 70.

Step 6: Determine the specific volume.

Obtaining the reading of the specific volume of the refrigerant is done at point "D". On this particular system, this value is about 1.5 ft³/lb. Point "D" on this plot lies right on the 1.5 ft³/lb line.

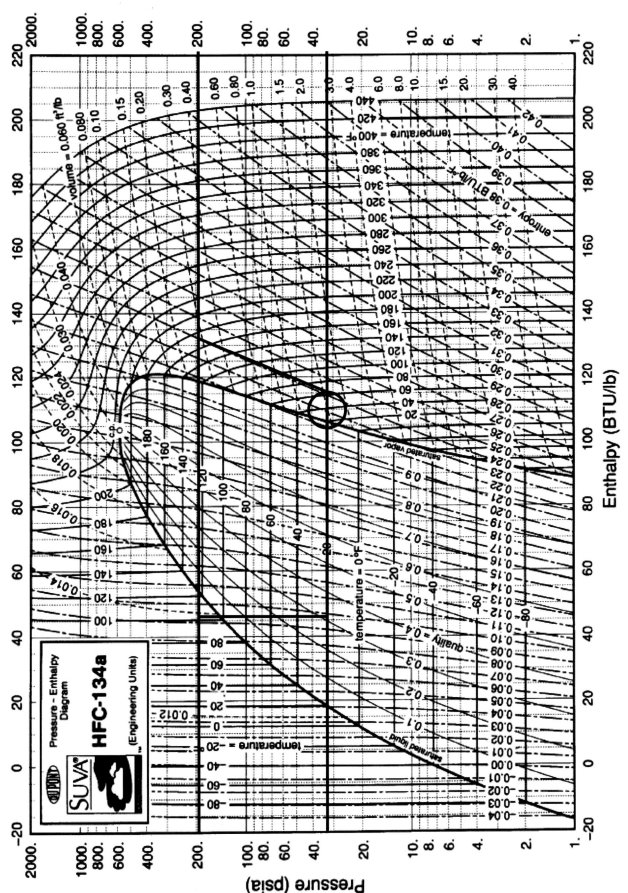

Figure 69. The evaporator outlet temperature of 40°F is the point where the 40-degee constant temperature line and the low side pressure lines cross. Pressure enthalpy chart courtesy DuPont.

101

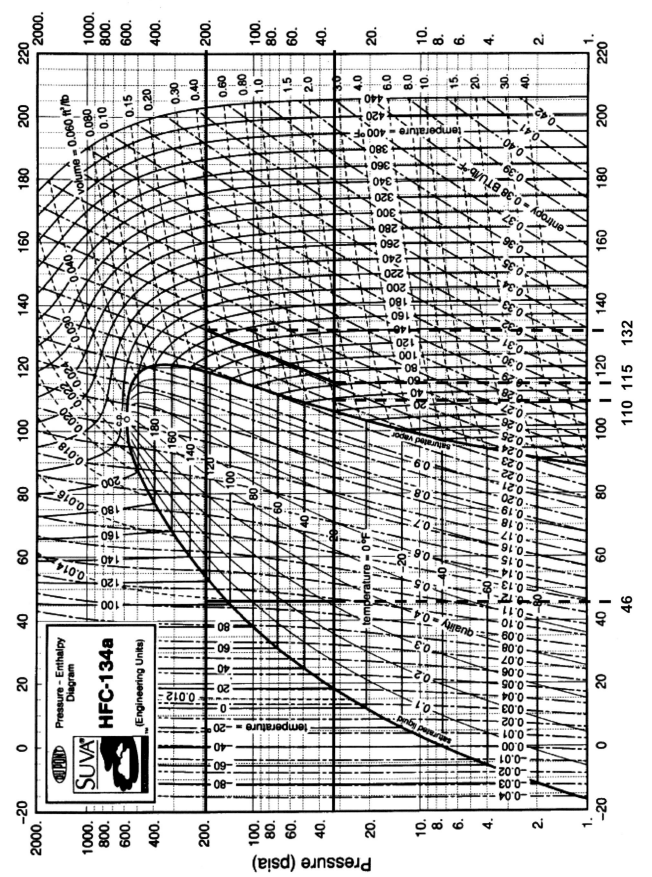

Figure 70. The completed pressure enthalpy plot for the medium temperature example. Pressure enthalpy chart courtesy DuPont.

Step 7: Perform the calculations.

Step 7a:Compression Ratio

Since we have the saturation temperatures, we can determine the saturation pressures from the pressure/temperature chart. The condenser saturation temperature of 120°F corresponds to a high side gauge pressure of 171 psig (186 psia) and the evaporator saturation temperature of 20°F corresponds to a low side gauge pressure of 18 psig (33 psia).

Compression Ratio= High Side (psia) ÷ Low Side (psia)
Compression Ratio = 186 psia ÷ 33 psia
Compression Ratio = 5.6:1

Step 7b: Net Refrigeration Effect, NRE

Net Refrigeration Effect, NRE= C – B
NRE = 110 btu/lb – 46 btu/lb
NRE = 64 btu/lb

Step 7c: Heat of Compression, HOC

Heat of Compression, HOC = E – C
HOC = 132 btu/lb – 110 btu/lb
HOC = 22 btu/lb

Step 7d: Heat of Work, HOW

Heat of Work, HOW = E – D
HOW = 132 btu/lb – 115 btu/lb
HOW = 17 btu/lb

Step 7e: Total Heat of Rejection, THOR

Total Heat of Rejection, THOR = E – A
THOR = 132 btu/lb – 46 btu/lb
THOR = 86 btu/lb

Step 7f: Coefficient of Performance, COP

Coefficient of Performance, COP = NRE ÷ HOC
COP = 64 btu/lb ÷ 22 btu/lb
COP = 2.9

Step 7g: Mass Flow Rate per Ton, MFR/ton

Mass Flow Rate per Ton, MFR/ton = 200 ÷ NRE
MFR/ton = 200 ÷ 64 btu/lb
MFR/ton = 3.13 lb/min/ton

Step 7h: Theoretical HP per ton, THp/ton

Theoretical HP per ton, THp/ton = (MFR/ton x HOW) ÷ 42.42
THp/ton = (3.13 lb/min/ton x 17 btu/lb) ÷ 42.42
THp/ton = 1.3 Hp/ton

Step 7i: Mass Flow Rate/System, MFR/system

Mass Flow Rate/System, MFR/system = 42.42 x Hp ÷ HOW
MFR/system = 42.42 x 5 ÷ HOW
MFR/system = 212.10 ÷ 17 btu/lb
MFR/system = 12.48 lb/min

Step 7j: Capacity of the Evaporator, btu/hour

Capacity of the Evaporator = MFR/system x NRE x 60
Capacity/evaporator = 12.48 lb/min x 64 btu/lb x 60 min/hour
Capacity/evaporator = 47,923 btu/hour

Step 7k: Capacity of the Evaporator, tons

Evaporator Tonnage = 47,923 btu/hour ÷ 12,000 btu/hour/ton
Evaporator Tonnage = 3.99 tons

Step 7l: Capacity of the Condenser, btu/hour

Capacity of the Condenser = MFR/system x THOR x 60
Capacity/condenser = 12.48 lb/min x 86 btu/lb x 60 min/hour
Capacity/condenser = 64,397 btu/hour

Step 7m: Capacity of the Condenser, tons

Condenser Tonnage = 64,397 btu/hour ÷ 12,000 btu/hour/ton
Condenser Tonnage = 5.37 tons

Step 7n: Capacity of the Compressor

Capacity of the Compressor = MFR/system x Specific Volume
Capacity/compressor = 12.48 lb/min x 1.5 ft^3/lb
Capacity/compressor = 18.72 ft^3/min

Step 7o: Energy Efficiency Ratio, EER

Energy Efficiency Ratio, EER = COP x 3.413
Energy Efficiency Ratio, EER = 2.9 x 3.413
Energy Efficiency Ratio, EER = 9.9

Step 7p: Seasonal Energy Efficiency Ratio, SEER – Low end of the range

Seasonal Energy Efficiency Ratio, SEER (low end) = 1.1 x EER
SEER (low end) = 1.1 x 9.9
SEER (low end) = 10.9

Step 7q: Seasonal Energy Efficiency Ratio, SEER – High end of the range

Seasonal Energy Efficiency Ratio, SEER (high end) = 1.3 x EER
SEER (high end) = 1.3 x 9.9
SEER (high end) = 12.87

SYSTEM #3: Defective Evaporator Fan Motor (medium temperature application)

This is the same system from example #2. The only difference is that the evaporator fan motor is defective. All of the high side system parameters have been kept constant so the effects of the inoperative fan motor can be more readily seen. The constant high side pressure is, in our example, justified by the use of a head pressure control that will maintain the high side pressure at 171 psig (120°F on the p/t chart). The system information is as follows:

Condenser saturation temperature: 120°F
Condenser outlet temperature: 100°F
Evaporator saturation temperature: -20°F
Evaporator outlet temperature: -20°F
Compressor inlet temperature: 15°F
Compressor horsepower: 5 Hp
System refrigerant: R-134a

As in the previous example, we will compute the following system parameters:

Compression Ratio	COP	CAP/cond
NRE	MFR/ton	CAP/comp
HOW	THp/ton	EER
HOC	MFR/system	SEER range
THOR	CAP/evap	

The completed plot for this system is shown in Figure 71.

The enthalpy values for this system are as follows:

Heat content at point "A": 46 btu/lb
Heat content at point "B": 46 btu/lb
Heat content at point "C": 101 btu/lb
Heat content at point "D": 107 btu/lb
Heat content at point "E": 132 btu/lb

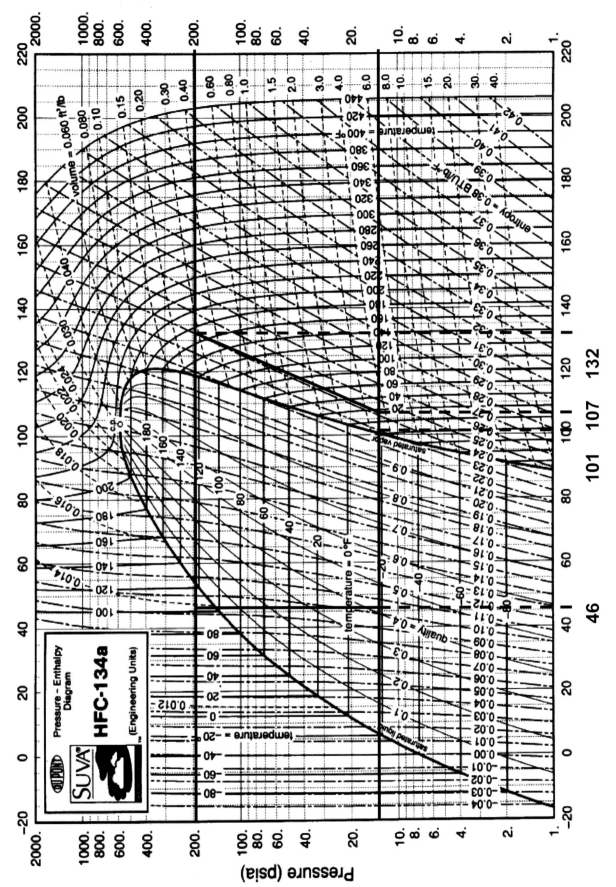

Figure 71. This medium temperature system is operating with a defective evaporator fan motor. Pressure enthalpy chart courtesy DuPont.

System #3: Calculations

Step 1a: Compression Ratio

Since we have the saturation temperatures, we can determine the saturation pressures from the pressure/temperature chart. The condenser saturation temperature of 120°F corresponds to a high side gauge pressure of 171 psig (186 psia) and the evaporator saturation temperature of -20°F corresponds to a low side gauge pressure of 3.6"Hg (13 psia). Refer back to the section on pressure conversions (page 19) for details on the conversion from of 3.6"Hg to 13 psia.

Compression Ratio= High Side (psia) ÷ Low Side (psia)
Compression Ratio = 186 psia ÷ 13 psia
Compression Ratio = 14.3:1

Step 1b: Net Refrigeration Effect, NRE

Net Refrigeration Effect, NRE= C – B
NRE = 101 btu/lb – 46 btu/lb
NRE = 55 btu/lb

Step 1c: Heat of Compression, HOC

Heat of Compression, HOC = E – C
HOC = 132 btu/lb – 101 btu/lb
HOC = 31 btu/lb

Step 1d: Heat of Work, HOW

Heat of Work, HOW = E – D
HOW = 132 btu/lb – 107 btu/lb
HOW = 25 btu/lb

Step 1e: Total Heat of Rejection, THOR

Total Heat of Rejection, THOR = E – A
THOR = 132 btu/lb – 46 btu/lb
THOR = 86 btu/lb

Step 1f: Coefficient of Performance, COP

Coefficient of Performance, COP = NRE ÷ HOC
COP = 55 btu/lb ÷ 31 btu/lb
COP = 1.8

Step 1g: Mass Flow Rate per Ton, MFR/ton

Mass Flow Rate per Ton, MFR/ton = 200 ÷ NRE
MFR/ton = 200 ÷ 55 btu/lb
MFR/ton = 3.64 lb/min/ton

Step 1h: Theoretical HP per ton, THp/ton

Theoretical HP per ton, THp/ton = (MFR/ton x HOW) ÷ 42.42
THp/ton = (3.64 lb/min/ton x 25 btu/lb) ÷ 42.42
THp/ton = 2.15 Hp/ton

Step 1i: Mass Flow Rate/System, MFR/system

Mass Flow Rate/System, MFR/system = 42.42 x Hp ÷ HOW
MFR/system = 42.42 x 5 ÷ HOW
MFR/system = 212.10 ÷ 25 btu/lb
MFR/system = 8.48 lb/min

Step 1j: Capacity of the Evaporator, btu/hour

Capacity of the Evaporator = MFR/system x NRE x 60
Capacity/evaporator = 8.48 lb/min x 55 btu/lb x 60 min/hour
Capacity/evaporator = 27,984 btu/hour

Step 1k: Capacity of the Evaporator, tons

Evaporator Tonnage = 27,984 btu/hour ÷ 12,000 btu/hour/ton
Evaporator Tonnage = 2.33 tons

Step 1l: Capacity of the Condenser, btu/hour

Capacity of the Condenser = MFR/system x THOR x 60
Capacity/condenser = 8.48 lb/min x 86 btu/lb x 60 min/hour
Capacity/condenser = 43,757 btu/hour

Step 1m: Capacity of the Condenser, tons

Condenser Tonnage = 43,757 btu/hour ÷ 12,000 btu/hour/ton
Condenser Tonnage = 3.65 tons

Step 1n: Capacity of the Compressor

Capacity of the Compressor = MFR/system x Specific Volume
Capacity/compressor = 8.48 lb/min x 3.8 ft^3/lb
Capacity/compressor = 32.2 ft^3/min

Step 1o: Energy Efficiency Ratio, EER

        Energy Efficiency Ratio, EER = COP x 3.413
        Energy Efficiency Ratio, EER = 1.8 x 3.413
        Energy Efficiency Ratio, EER = 6.14

Step 1p: Seasonal Energy Efficiency Ratio, SEER – Low end of the range

        Seasonal Energy Efficiency Ratio, SEER (low end) = 1.1 x EER
        SEER (low end) = 1.1 x 6.14
        SEER (low end) = 6.75

Step 1q: Seasonal Energy Efficiency Ratio, SEER – High end of the range

        Seasonal Energy Efficiency Ratio, SEER (high end) = 1.3 x EER
        SEER (high end) = 1.3 x 6.14
        SEER (high end) = 7.98

SYSTEM COMPARISON: SYSTEM #2 VS. SYSTEM #3

Since system #2 and system #3 are identical, with the exception of the malfunctioning evaporator fan motor, we will now compare the results and calculations to determine the effects of the system malfunction on system performance. The results of the calculations are presented in the following table:

	SYSTEM #2	SYSTEM #3	
	Normal Operation	Defective Evap. Fan Motor	Increase, Decrease, Remain the Same
Compression Ratio	5.6:1	14.3:1	**Increase**
NRE	64 btu/lb	55 btu/lb	Decrease
HOC	22 btu/lb	31 btu/lb	**Increase**
HOW	17 btu/lb	25 btu/lb	**Increase**
THOR	86 btu/lb	86 btu/lb	Remain the Same
COP	2.9	1.8	Decrease
MFR/ton	3.13 lb/min/ton	3.64 lb/min/ton	**Increase**
THp/Ton	1.3 Hp/ton	2.15 Hp/ton	**Increase**
MFR/system	12.48 lb/min	8.48 lb/min	Decrease
Evaporator Capacity	47,923 btu/hour	27,984 btu/hour	Decrease
Evaporator Tonnage	3.99 tons	2.33 tons	Decrease
Condenser Capacity	64,397 btu/hour	43,757 btu/hour	Decrease
Condenser Tonnage	5.37 tons	3.65 tons	Decrease
Capacity/compressor	18.72 ft^3/min	32.2 ft^3/min	**Increase**
EER	9.9	6.14	Decrease
SEER (low end)	10.9	6.75	Decrease
SEER (high end)	12.87	7.98	Decrease

Compression Ratio

In both sample system #2 and system #3, the head pressure remained the same. This was due to the head pressure control that was installed on the system. System #2 was operating properly, but system #3 had a defective evaporator fan motor, which resulted in reduced airflow across the evaporator coil surface. This reduction in airflow reduced the amount of heat added to the refrigerant as the air is the source of heat which the evaporator absorbs. Furthermore, this reduction in heat will cause the saturation temperature and pressure of the refrigerant to fall.

By reducing the evaporator saturation pressure, the distance between the high side pressure and the low side pressure increases, causing the compression ratio to increase. An increase in compression ratio leads to an increase in the heat of work and a reduction in the net refrigeration effect and the mass flow rate, Figure 72.

Any increase in head pressure or decrease in the suction pressure will cause the compression ratio to increase, while a decrease in head pressure or an increase in suction pressure will cause the compression ratio to increase.

Here's a not-so-true story that relates to compression ratios.

I have a very good friend named Tammy. She is an administrative assistant for a law firm that has its offices in a hi-rise office building. The law firm has two offices; one on the second floor and one on the 93rd floor. Tammy works for two lawyers and yes, you guessed it, one of the lawyers works on the 2nd floor and the other works on the 93rd floor. By the way, did I mention that the building has no elevators?

Now here is an average work day for Tammy. Tammy arrives at the building at 9:00 am and reports to the 2nd floor office and begins her day by working for the 2nd floor lawyer for one hour. After that hour has elapsed, Tammy walks up to the 93rd floor and works for the 93rd floor lawyer for an hour. She then walks down the stairs to the 2nd floor and so on.

As a result of this logistical nightmare, Tammy spends a great deal of time walking up and down stairs. Although, according to her, she is working, she is not doing productive work for the law firm. One day Tammy's boss realized this and decided to move the 93rd floor office to the 3rd floor. As a result, Tammy did much more productive work as she spent less time walking up and down the stairs.

Now, consider a reciprocating compressor that has to increase and decrease the pressure of the refrigerant in the compression cylinder before it can discharge compressed refrigerant or accept new refrigerant from the suction line. The compressor's job after all is the facilitate the flow of refrigerant in the system. If the compression ratio is low, the compressor, like Tammy, can spend less time running up and down and more time doing useful work.

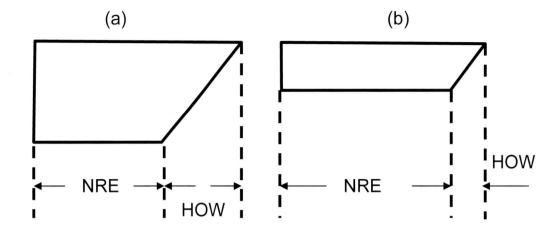

Figure 72. (a) A system with a high compression ratio will have a larger heat of work, which results in a lower mass flow rate for the system. (b) A lower compression ratio reduces the heat of work and facilitates a higher mass flow rate for the system.

Net Refrigeration Effect

At a constant liquid line temperature, the NRE will fall as the evaporator saturation temperature drops. This is because the edges of the saturation curve on the pressure enthalpy chart slope to the right. Also note that the compressor line, which follows, for the most part, a line of constant entropy is also sloped.

As we move further down toward the bottom of the chart the net refrigeration effect will get smaller and smaller. So, as the low side pressure on a system falls lower and lower, the number of btu/lb picked up in the evaporator drops as well, Figure 72, assuming other system factors remain the same.

Heat of Compression

Since we kept the high side components of the system the same, the total heat of rejection remained the same as well. Total heat of rejection is the sum of the NRE and the HOC. Because the NRE has gotten smaller as a result of the falling suction temperature and pressure, the remaining component of THOR, HOC, gets larger. The larger HOC is due to the increase in the heat of work, Figure 72.

Heat of Work

The heat of work of a system is directly related to the compression ratio. A larger compression ratio leads to a larger heat of work and a smaller compression ratio leads to a smaller heat of work, Figure 72. The increase in the heat of work has an effect not only on the NRE, but also on the mass flow rate of the system, as the heat of work is a direct component of that calculation.

Side note:

> So far, having evaluated the compression ratio, NRE, HOW and HOC, we have seen that all of the negative factors (compression ratio, HOW and HOC) have increased, while the positive factor (NRE) has gotten smaller. It should be getting clearer how all of these system parameters are interconnected and a change in one will likely have an effect on the others.

Total Heat of Rejection

The total heat of rejection for both system #2 and system #3 remained the same. In reality this will not likely be the case but, for illustrative purposes, this system parameter was intentionally left unchanged to allow the reader to easily visualize the effects of the system malfunction. Since the THOR remained the same and it is made up of the NRE and the HOC, a decrease in either the NRE or HOC will result in an increase in the other parameter.

Coefficient of Performance

The coefficient of performance is a ratio of efficiency and compares the beneficial output (NRE) to the heat equivalent of the work required to obtain that cooling effect. Any increase in NRE or decrease in HOC will result in an increase in the COP. Conversely, any decrease in NRE or increase in HOC will result in a decrease in COP. Notice how the COP decreased from 2.9 in our normal system to 1.8 in our defective fan motor example. This result was entirely expected because the NRE dropped from 64 btu/lb to 55 btu/lb (a 15% decrease) and the HOC increased from 24 btu/lb to 31 btu/lb (a 29% increase).

Mass Flow Rate per Ton

The MFR/ton tells us how many pounds of refrigerant must be circulated through the system per minute in order to obtain one ton of refrigeration. This system parameter is directly affected by the NRE and has an inverse relationship to it. An increase in NRE results in a decrease in MFR/ton and vice versa.

Be comparing system #2 and system #3 we can see that the NRE dropped in the case of the defective evaporator fan motor, so the MFR/ton increased. A higher-than-normal MFR/ton indicates a system deficiency as more refrigerant must be circulated to obtain the same ton of refrigeration. This also indicates that the compressor must work harder, or at least attempt to, to maintain the space being cooled at the desired temperature.

Theoretical Horsepower per Ton

Notice also that the theoretical horsepower per ton has also increased in the defective fan motor example. This is due to the fact that the THp/ton is directly related to the MFR/ton and the HOW of the system.

$$\text{Theoretical HP per ton, THp/ton} = (\text{MFR/ton} \times \text{HOW}) \div 42.42$$

Since the HOW rose as a result of the increased compression ratio and the MFR/ton increased as a result of the decreased NRE, the increase in THp/ton logically follows. Since the number of motor horsepower to provide one ton of refrigeration increases and the actual motor horsepower remains the same, it can then be concluded that the system (evaporator) capacity will fall as there is not enough motor power to provide the system's design capacity.

In system #2, the THp/ton is 1.3. Under those system conditions, if we wanted one ton of refrigeration, we would need a compressor with a 1.3 horsepower motor. Now, when the evaporator fan motor stopped operating, we would need a compressor with a 2.15 horsepower motor (the THp/ton from system #3) to give us the same one ton of refrigeration.

Mass Flow Rate of the System

The mass flow rate of the system is determined by the motor horsepower and the heat of work. Since the compressor motor horsepower does not change when the system's operating conditions change, it can be said that the only system variable that affects the mass flow rate of the system is the HOW:

$$\text{Mass Flow Rate/System, MFR/system} = 42.42 \times \text{Hp} \div \text{HOW}$$

So, as the compression ratio increases, so does the heat of work. An increase in the heat of work results in a decrease in the rate of refrigerant flow through the system. As the amount of refrigerant flowing in the system decreases, the heat transfer rates also decrease and the capacities of the evaporator and condenser drop as well.

Notice that, when comparing systems #2 and #3, that the MFR/system dropped 32%, from 12.48 lb/min to only 8.48 lb/min. This resulted in a significant drop in evaporator (system) capacity.

Capacity of the Evaporator

The capacity of the evaporator is determined by the NRE and the MFR/system:

Evaporator Capacity = NRE x MFR/system x 60

Because of the increased compression ratio for system #3, the NRE decreased. In addition to the smaller NRE, the heat of work increased, causing the MFR/system to decrease as well. Reducing the NRE and the HOW will, therefore, result in a decrease in system (evaporator) capacity, as the only other factor in the equation is the constant conversion factor of 60.

Capacity of the Condenser

It can be seen from the table on page 110 that the capacity of the condenser has also dropped. This is the case even though the THOR for both system #2 and system #3 remained the same. Since the THOR is the same and the conversion factor of 60 remains the same, the reduction in condenser capacity is due to the reduced MFR/system:

Condenser Capacity = THOR x MFR/system x 60

By keeping the THOR constant, the number of btu/lb that is rejected by the condenser is the same. What has changed is the number of pounds of refrigerant that are flowing through the system every minute. Once again, the MFR/system has been reduced as a result of the increased compression ratio and the increased heat of work.

Capacity of the Compressor

The increase in this parameter may be somewhat puzzling at first. The system capacity decreased but the compressor capacity increased. What we are referring to here is the required volume of vapor refrigerant that the compressor must move in order to reach the required mass flow rate.

As the evaporator saturation temperature falls, the specific volume of the refrigerant increases. This means that the density of the refrigerant is dropping and more cubic feet of vapor are required to make up one pound of refrigerant. For example, in system #2, the specific volume of the refrigerant entering the compressor was 1.5 ft^3/lb. So, in order for the compressor to move one pound of refrigerant, it had to move 1.5 cubic feet of vapor. As the suction pressure dropped in system #3, the specific volume rose to 3.8 ft^3/lb. Now, in order to move the same pound of refrigerant, the compressor had to move almost four cubic feet of vapor. For this reason, the compressor must work much harder to attempt to keep the system cooling.

It should also be noted that, even though the MFR/system dropped in system #3, the compressor capacity increased. This is because the specific volume rose faster than the MFR/system fell.

EER and SEER

The energy efficiency ratio and the seasonal energy efficiency ratio are both reliant on the performance parameter of the system; namely the COP:

$$COP = NRE \div HOC$$

Since the NRE decreased in system #3 and the HOC increased in the same system, it is safe to assume that the COP for system #3 will drop. And, from the charted results, this proves to be true. Recall that the COP is a ratio that compares the benefit received (in the form of cooling) compared to the heat equivalent of the cost of that benefit. In the case of system #3 the benefit decreased and the cost increased.

Because the COP for system #3 fell, it follows logically that the EER and SEER range for that system will be lower than those for system #2.

SYSTEM #4: System Undercharge (Air conditioning application)

Our next system is an R-22 system that is undercharged as a result of a refrigerant leak. The system is operating with a capillary tube metering device. This is a standard efficiency system and the operating conditions are as follows:

Temperature of the conditioned space: 80°F
Outside ambient temperature: 95°F
Condenser saturation temperature: 100°F
Condenser outlet temperature: 96°F
Evaporator saturation temperature: 27°F
Evaporator outlet temperature: 52°F
Compressor discharge temperature: 220°F
Compressor motor horsepower: 5 Hp

The completed plot for this system is shown in Figure 73.

The enthalpy values for this system are as follows:

Heat content at point "A": 36 btu/lb
Heat content at point "B": 36 btu/lb
Heat content at point "C": 113 btu/lb
Heat content at point "D": 122 btu/lb
Heat content at point "E": 137 btu/lb

Here are the system calculations:

Compression Ratio

The condenser saturation temperature of 100°F corresponds to a high side gauge pressure of 196 psig (211 psia) and the evaporator saturation temperature of 27°F corresponds to a low side gauge pressure of 51psig (66 psia).

Compression Ratio= High Side (psia) ÷ Low Side (psia)
Compression Ratio = 211 psia ÷ 66 psia
Compression Ratio = 3.2:1

Net Refrigeration Effect, NRE

Net Refrigeration Effect, NRE= C – B
NRE = 113 btu/lb – 36 btu/lb
NRE = 77 btu/lb

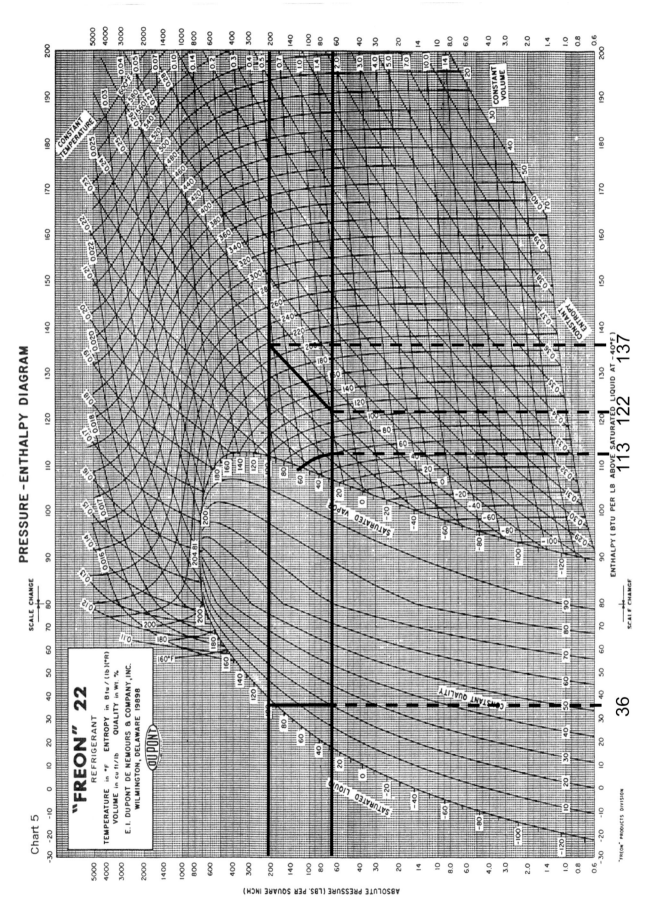

Figure 73. Undercharged R-22 air conditioning system. Pressure enthalpy chart courtesy DuPont.

118

Heat of Compression, HOC

       Heat of Compression, HOC = E – C
       HOC = 137 btu/lb – 113 btu/lb
       HOC = 24 btu/lb

Heat of Work, HOW

       Heat of Work, HOW = E – D
       HOW = 137 btu/lb – 122 btu/lb
       HOW = 15 btu/lb

Total Heat of Rejection, THOR

       Total Heat of Rejection, THOR = E – A
       THOR = 137 btu/lb – 36 btu/lb
       THOR = 101 btu/lb

Coefficient of Performance, COP

       Coefficient of Performance, COP = NRE ÷ HOC
       COP = 77 btu/lb ÷ 24 btu/lb
       COP = 3.2

Mass Flow Rate per Ton, MFR/ton

       Mass Flow Rate per Ton, MFR/ton = 200 ÷ NRE
       MFR/ton = 200 ÷ 77 btu/lb
       MFR/ton = 2.6 lb/min/ton

Theoretical HP per ton, THp/ton

       Theoretical HP per ton, THp/ton = (MFR/ton x HOW) ÷ 42.42
       THp/ton = (2.6 lb/min/ton x 15 btu/lb) ÷ 42.42
       THp/ton = 0.92 Hp/ton

Mass Flow Rate/System, MFR/system

       Mass Flow Rate/System, MFR/system = 42.42 x Hp ÷ HOW
       MFR/system = 42.42 x 5 ÷ HOW
       MFR/system = 212.1 ÷ 15 btu/lb
       MFR/system = 14.14 lb/min

Capacity of the Evaporator, btu/hour

> Capacity of the Evaporator = MFR/system x NRE x 60
> Capacity/evaporator = 14.14 lb/min x 77 btu/lb x 60 min/hour
> Capacity/evaporator = 65,327 btu/hour

Capacity of the Evaporator, tons

> Evaporator Tonnage = 65,327 btu/hour ÷ 12,000 btu/hour/ton
> Evaporator Tonnage = 5.4 tons

Capacity of the Condenser, btu/hour

> Capacity of the Condenser = MFR/system x THOR x 60
> Capacity/condenser = 14.14 lb/min x 101 btu/lb x 60 min/hour
> Capacity/condenser = 85,688 btu/hour

Capacity of the Condenser, tons

> Condenser Tonnage = 85,688 btu/hour ÷ 12,000 btu/hour/ton
> Condenser Tonnage = 7.1 tons

Capacity of the Compressor

> Capacity of the Compressor = MFR/system x Specific Volume
> Capacity/compressor = 14.14 lb/min x 1.0 ft^3/lb
> Capacity/compressor = 14.14 ft^3/min

Energy Efficiency Ratio, EER

> Energy Efficiency Ratio, EER = COP x 3.413
> Energy Efficiency Ratio, EER = 3.2 x 3.413
> Energy Efficiency Ratio, EER = 10.9

Seasonal Energy Efficiency Ratio, SEER – Low end of the range

> Seasonal Energy Efficiency Ratio, SEER (low end) = 1.1 x EER
> SEER (low end) = 1.1 x 10.9
> SEER (low end) = 11.99

Seasonal Energy Efficiency Ratio, SEER – High end of the range

> Seasonal Energy Efficiency Ratio, SEER (high end) = 1.3 x EER
> SEER (high end) = 1.3 x 10.9
> SEER (high end) = 14.17

SYSTEM COMPARISON: SYSTEM #1 VS. SYSTEM #4

The following table shows the results of the calculations for system #1 and system #4. System #1 was a properly operating air conditioning system with a 5 horsepower compressor operating on a 95°F day. System #4 is the same system, but is operating with a refrigerant undercharge. By comparing the physical appearances of the two pressure enthalpy plots, it appears that the plot for the system operating with the low refrigerant charge is the same as the plot of the normally operating system with the exception that the undercharged system plot has been shifted downward. For the most part, this is indeed the case, but it should also be noted that the compressor discharge temperature has increased significantly. This will prove to be an important factor in our evaluation.

	SYSTEM #1	SYSTEM #4	
	Normal Operation (Air Conditioning)	System Undercharge	Increase, Decrease, Remain the Same
Compression Ratio	3.53:1	3.2:1	**Decrease**
NRE	70 btu/lb	77 btu/lb	Increase
HOC	18 btu/lb	24 btu/lb	Increase
HOW	14 btu/lb	15 btu/lb	Increase
THOR	88 btu/lb	101 btu/lb	Increase
COP	3.9	3.2	**Decrease**
MFR/ton	2.86 lb/min/ton	2.6 lb/min/ton	**Decrease**
THp/Ton	0.94 Hp/ton	0.92 Hp/ton	**Decrease**
MFR/system	15.15 lb/min	14.14 lb/min	**Decrease**
Evaporator Capacity	63,630 btu/hour	65,327 btu/hour	Increase
Evaporator Tonnage	5.3 tons	5.4 tons	Increase
Condenser Capacity	79,992 btu/hour	85,688 btu/hour	Increase
Condenser Tonnage	6.67 tons	7.1 tons	Increase
Capacity/compressor	10.6 ft^3/min	14.14 ft^3/min	Increase
EER	13.3	10.9	**Decrease**
SEER (low end)	14.63	11.99	**Decrease**
SEER (high end)	17.3	14.17	**Decrease**

By comparing the calculated values for the normally operating system with those of the system with the refrigerant undercharge, it can be seen that the system actually experiences some benefits in the form of decreased compression ratio, MFR/ton and THp/ton. In addition, the capacity of the evaporator also rose from 5.3 tons to 5.4 tons (a 1.9% increase in capacity). This increase in system capacity goes unnoticed, but the negative effects become more obvious to the equipment owner or operator.

The decrease in COP from 3.9 to 3.2 indicates a large decrease in system efficiency, as indicated by the 18% drop in EER. A 1.0% increase in system capacity is hardly worth the increased operating costs related to the 18% drop in EER.

SYSTEM #5: R-410A System (Air conditioning application)

The following chart will represent an R-410A system that is operating with exactly the same operating conditions as those used for our normally operating, high temperature R-22 system in system #1 on page 82. We can then compare the results of both systems and establish the differences between identical systems operating with different refrigerants. So, we have the following conditions for our R-410A system:

Condenser Saturation Pressure: 446 psig (equal to 278 psig for R-22)
Evaporator Saturation Pressure: 118 psig (equal to 68.5 psig for R-22)
Evaporator Outlet Temperature: 50°F
Condenser Outlet Temperature: 100°F
Compressor Discharge Temperature: 180°F
System has a 5 Horsepower reciprocating compressor

The completed plot is shown in Figure 74.

The enthalpy values for this system are as follows:

Heat content at point "A": 46 btu/lb
Heat content at point "B": 46 btu/lb
Heat content at point "C": 125 btu/lb
Heat content at point "D": 128 btu/lb
Heat content at point "E": 144 btu/lb

Here are the system calculations:

Compression Ratio

The condenser saturation temperature of 125°F corresponds to a high side gauge pressure of 446 psig (461 psia) and the evaporator saturation temperature of 40°F corresponds to a low side gauge pressure of 118 psig (133 psia).

Compression Ratio= High Side (psia) ÷ Low Side (psia)
Compression Ratio = 461 psia ÷ 133 psia
Compression Ratio = 3.5:1

Net Refrigeration Effect, NRE

Net Refrigeration Effect, NRE= C – B
NRE = 125 btu/lb – 53 btu/lb
NRE = 72 btu/lb

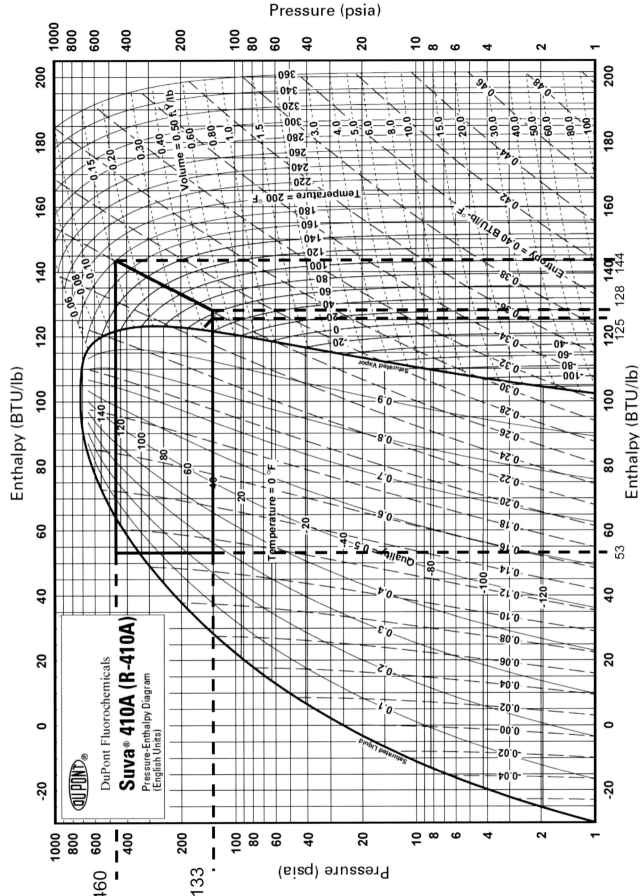

Figure 74. An R-410A air conditioning system operating with a 40-degree evaporator coil temperature. Pressure enthalpy chart courtesy DuPont.

123

Heat of Compression, HOC

Heat of Compression, HOC = E – C
HOC = 143 btu/lb – 125 btu/lb
HOC = 18 btu/lb

Heat of Work, HOW

Heat of Work, HOW = E – D
HOW = 143 btu/lb – 128 btu/lb
HOW = 15 btu/lb

Total Heat of Rejection, THOR

Total Heat of Rejection, THOR = E – A
THOR = 143 btu/lb – 53 btu/lb
THOR = 90 btu/lb

Coefficient of Performance, COP

Coefficient of Performance, COP = NRE ÷ HOC
COP = 72 btu/lb ÷ 18 btu/lb
COP = 4.00

Mass Flow Rate per Ton, MFR/ton

Mass Flow Rate per Ton, MFR/ton = 200 ÷ NRE
MFR/ton = 200 ÷ 72 btu/lb
MFR/ton = 2.78 lb/min/ton

Theoretical HP per ton, THp/ton

Theoretical HP per ton, THp/ton = (MFR/ton x HOW) ÷ 42.42
THp/ton = (2.78 lb/min/ton x 15 btu/lb) ÷ 42.42
THp/ton = 0.98 Hp/ton

Mass Flow Rate/System, MFR/system

Mass Flow Rate/System, MFR/system = 42.42 x Hp ÷ HOW
MFR/system = 42.42 x 5 ÷ HOW
MFR/system = 212.1 ÷ 15 btu/lb
MFR/system = 14.14 lb/min

Capacity of the Evaporator, btu/hour

Capacity of the Evaporator = MFR/system x NRE x 60
Capacity/evaporator = 14.14 lb/min x 72 btu/lb x 60 min/hour
Capacity/evaporator = 61,085 btu/hour

Capacity of the Evaporator, tons

Evaporator Tonnage = 61,085 btu/hour ÷ 12,000 btu/hour/ton
Evaporator Tonnage = 5.09 tons

Capacity of the Condenser, btu/hour

Capacity of the Condenser = MFR/system x THOR x 60
Capacity/condenser = 14.14 lb/min x 90 btu/lb x 60 min/hour
Capacity/condenser = 76,356 btu/hour

Capacity of the Condenser, tons

Condenser Tonnage = 76,356 btu/hour ÷ 12,000 btu/hour/ton
Condenser Tonnage = 6.36 tons

Capacity of the Compressor

Capacity of the Compressor = MFR/system x Specific Volume
Capacity/compressor = 14.14 lb/min x 0.5 ft^3/lb
Capacity/compressor = 7.07 ft^3/min

Energy Efficiency Ratio, EER

Energy Efficiency Ratio, EER = COP x 3.413
Energy Efficiency Ratio, EER = 4.00 x 3.413
Energy Efficiency Ratio, EER = 13.69

Seasonal Energy Efficiency Ratio, SEER – Low end of the range

Seasonal Energy Efficiency Ratio, SEER (low end) = 1.1 x EER
SEER (low end) = 1.1 x 13.69
SEER (low end) = 15.06

Seasonal Energy Efficiency Ratio, SEER – High end of the range

Seasonal Energy Efficiency Ratio, SEER (high end) = 1.3 x EER
SEER (high end) = 1.3 x 13.69
SEER (high end) = 17.8

SYSTEM COMPARISON: SYSTEM #1 VS. SYSTEM #5

The following table shows the results of the calculations for system #1 and system #5. System #1 was a properly operating air conditioning system with a 5 horsepower compressor operating on a 95°F day. System #5 is the same system, but is operating with R-410A as its refrigerant.

	SYSTEM #1	SYSTEM #5	
	R-22 Normal Operation (Air Conditioning)	R-410A Normal Operation (Air Conditioning)	Increase, Decrease, Remain the Same
Compression Ratio	3.53:1	3.5:1	**Decrease**
NRE	70 btu/lb	72 btu/lb	Increase
HOC	18 btu/lb	18 btu/lb	Remain the Same
HOW	14 btu/lb	15 btu/lb	Increase
THOR	88 btu/lb	90 btu/lb	Increase
COP	3.89	4.00	Increase
MFR/ton	2.86 lb/min/ton	2.78 lb/min/ton	**Decrease**
THp/Ton	0.94 Hp/ton	0.98 Hp/ton	Increase
MFR/system	15.15 lb/min	14.14 lb/min	**Decrease**
Evaporator Capacity	63,630 btu/hour	61,085 btu/hour	**Decrease**
Evaporator Tonnage	5.3 tons	5.09 tons	**Decrease**
Condenser Capacity	79,992 btu/hour	76,356 btu/hour	**Decrease**
Condenser Tonnage	6.67 tons	6.36 tons	**Decrease**
Capacity/compressor	10.6 ft^3/min	7.07 ft^3/min	**Decrease**
EER	13.3	13.69	Increase
SEER (low end)	14.63	15.06	Increase
SEER (high end)	17.3	17.8	Increase

Under these system conditions, the system (evaporator) capacity remained relatively constant (within 0.2 ton), while the SEER increased by about 3 percent. It can also be seen that a number of the system parameters such as compression ratio, HOC, THp/ton, remained relatively constant. It can be seen that using R-410A under these conditions results in higher system efficiency. The next system example will be identical to the R-410A system #5, with the exception that a 45-degree evaporator coil will be used. Typically R-410A air conditioning systems operate with an evaporator coil temperature that is slightly higher than the commonly accepted 40- degree coil found on conventional air conditioning systems.

SYSTEM #6: R-410A System (Air conditioning application)

The following chart will represent an R-410A system that is operating with a 45-degree evaporator coil temperature. We will then compare the results of this system to the results obtained from system #5 to establish the change in system operation when relatively seemingly minor changes are made to the operating conditions. So, we have the following conditions for our R-410A system:

Condenser Saturation Pressure: 446 psig (equal to 278 psig for R-22)
Evaporator Saturation Pressure: 130 psig (45°F evaporator saturation temperature)
Evaporator Outlet Temperature: 60°F
Condenser Outlet Temperature: 100°F
Compressor Discharge Temperature: 170°F
System has a 5 Horsepower reciprocating compressor

The completed plot is shown in Figure 75.

The enthalpy values for this system are as follows:

> Heat content at point "A": 53 btu/lb
> Heat content at point "B": 53 btu/lb
> Heat content at point "C": 125 btu/lb
> Heat content at point "D": 125 btu/lb
> Heat content at point "E": 141 btu/lb

Here are the system calculations:

Compression Ratio

> The condenser saturation temperature of 125°F corresponds to a high side gauge pressure of 446 psig (461 psia) and the evaporator saturation temperature of 40°F corresponds to a low side gauge pressure of 130 psig (145 psia).
>
> Compression Ratio= High Side (psia) ÷ Low Side (psia)
> Compression Ratio = 461 psia ÷ 145 psia
> Compression Ratio = 3.18:1

Net Refrigeration Effect, NRE

> Net Refrigeration Effect, NRE= C – B
> NRE = 125 btu/lb – 53 btu/lb
> NRE = 72 btu/lb

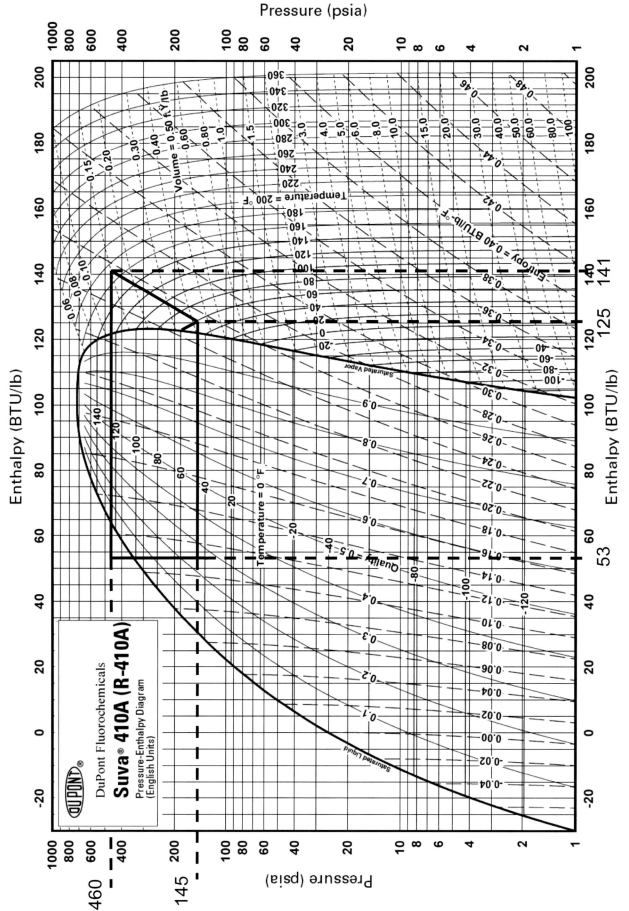

Figure 75. An R-410A air conditioning system operating with a 45-degree evaporator coil temperature. Pressure enthalpy chart courtesy DuPont.

128

Heat of Compression, HOC

> Heat of Compression, HOC = E − C
> HOC = 141 btu/lb − 125 btu/lb
> HOC = 16 btu/lb

Heat of Work, HOW

> Heat of Work, HOW = E − D
> HOW = 141 btu/lb − 125 btu/lb
> HOW = 16 btu/lb

Total Heat of Rejection, THOR

> Total Heat of Rejection, THOR = E − A
> THOR = 141 btu/lb − 53 btu/lb
> THOR = 88 btu/lb

Coefficient of Performance, COP

> Coefficient of Performance, COP = NRE ÷ HOC
> COP = 72 btu/lb ÷ 16 btu/lb
> COP = 4.5

Mass Flow Rate per Ton, MFR/ton

> Mass Flow Rate per Ton, MFR/ton = 200 ÷ NRE
> MFR/ton = 200 ÷ 72 btu/lb
> MFR/ton = 2.78 lb/min/ton

Theoretical HP per ton, THp/ton

> Theoretical HP per ton, THp/ton = (MFR/ton x HOW) ÷ 42.42
> THp/ton = (2.78 lb/min/ton x 16 btu/lb) ÷ 42.42
> THp/ton = 1.05 Hp/ton

Mass Flow Rate/System, MFR/system

> Mass Flow Rate/System, MFR/system = 42.42 x Hp ÷ HOW
> MFR/system = 42.42 x 5 ÷ HOW
> MFR/system = 212.1 ÷ 16 btu/lb
> MFR/system = 13.26 lb/min

Capacity of the Evaporator, btu/hour

Capacity of the Evaporator = MFR/system x NRE x 60
Capacity/evaporator = 13.26 lb/min x 72 btu/lb x 60 min/hour
Capacity/evaporator = 57,283 btu/hour

Capacity of the Evaporator, tons

Evaporator Tonnage = 57,283 btu/hour ÷ 12,000 btu/hour/ton
Evaporator Tonnage = 4.8 tons

Capacity of the Condenser, btu/hour

Capacity of the Condenser = MFR/system x THOR x 60
Capacity/condenser = 13.26 lb/min x 88 btu/lb x 60 min/hour
Capacity/condenser = 70,013 btu/hour

Capacity of the Condenser, tons

Condenser Tonnage = 70,013 btu/hour ÷ 12,000 btu/hour/ton
Condenser Tonnage = 5.8 tons

Capacity of the Compressor

Capacity of the Compressor = MFR/system x Specific Volume
Capacity/compressor = 13.26 lb/min x 0.42 ft^3/lb
Capacity/compressor = 5.6 ft^3/min

Energy Efficiency Ratio, EER

Energy Efficiency Ratio, EER = COP x 3.413
Energy Efficiency Ratio, EER = 4.5 x 3.413
Energy Efficiency Ratio, EER = 15.36

Seasonal Energy Efficiency Ratio, SEER – Low end of the range

Seasonal Energy Efficiency Ratio, SEER (low end) = 1.1 x EER
SEER (low end) = 1.1 x 15.36
SEER (low end) = 16.9

Seasonal Energy Efficiency Ratio, SEER – High end of the range

Seasonal Energy Efficiency Ratio, SEER (high end) = 1.3 x EER
SEER (high end) = 1.3 x 15.36
SEER (high end) = 19.97

SYSTEM COMPARISON: SYSTEM #5 VS. SYSTEM #6

The following table shows the results of the calculations for system #1 and system #5. System #1 was a properly operating air conditioning system with a 5 horsepower compressor operating on a 95°F day. System #5 is the same system, but is operating with R-410A as its refrigerant.

	SYSTEM #5	SYSTEM #6	
	R-410A Normal Operation (Air Conditioning with 40-degree evaporator coil)	R-410A Normal Operation (Air Conditioning with 45-degree evaporator coil)	Increase, Decrease, Remain the Same
Compression Ratio	3.5:1	3.18:1	Decrease
NRE	72 btu/lb	72 btu/lb	Remain the same
HOC	18 btu/lb	16 btu/lb	Decrease
HOW	15 btu/lb	16 btu/lb	Increase
THOR	90 btu/lb	88 btu/lb	Decrease
COP	4.00	4.5	Increase
MFR/ton	2.78 lb/min/ton	2.78 lb/min/ton	Remain the same
THp/Ton	0.98 Hp/ton	1.05 Hp/ton	Increase
MFR/system	14.14 lb/min	13.26 lb/min	Decrease
Evaporator Capacity	61,085 btu/hour	57,283 btu/hour	Decrease
Evaporator Tonnage	5.09 tons	4.77 tons	Decrease
Condenser Capacity	76,356 btu/hour	70,013 btu/hour	Decrease
Condenser Tonnage	6.36 tons	5.8 tons	Decrease
Capacity/compressor	7.07 ft^3/min	5.6 ft^3/min	Decrease
EER	13.69	15.36	Increase
SEER (low end)	15.06	16.9	Increase
SEER (high end)	17.8	19.97	Increase

Under these system conditions, the system (evaporator) capacity dropped slightly, along with a large number of other system parameters. The SEER increased by over 12 percent. The main purpose of this comparison is to show that even small changes in system operating conditions can have profound effects on the amount of energy being consumed by these systems. It should be further noted that, as can be seen from the evaporator capacity calculations, that the equipment owner will not notice any changes in operation if the energy costs are not evaluated. In addition, the wear and tear on the compressor and mechanical system components is greatly reduced can be seen by the compressor capacity calculations.

The following pages contain blank pressure enthalpy charts for the following refrigerants:

R-22
R-134a
R-410A
R-123
R-407C
MP-39 (R-401A)

More information on pressure enthalpy plots can be found at www.dupont.com. Search "pressure enthalpy chart".

The following additional resources may prove useful:

http://www.honeywell.com/sites/sm/chemicals/genetron

http://www.refron.com

http://www.refrigerants.com

http://www.refrigerants.com/catalog.pdf

You can also use the following contacts for Eugene Silberstein:

e-mail: silbere@sunysuffolk.edu

e-mail: eugene.silberstein@yahoo.com

THE HVAC PROF, INC.
150 Farm Road East
Wading River, NY 11792

You can also visit Eugene's bulletin board, "Ask Professor Silberstein" on THE WALL at www.heatinghelp.com by simply clicking on the "QUESTIONS" icon at the top of the home page.

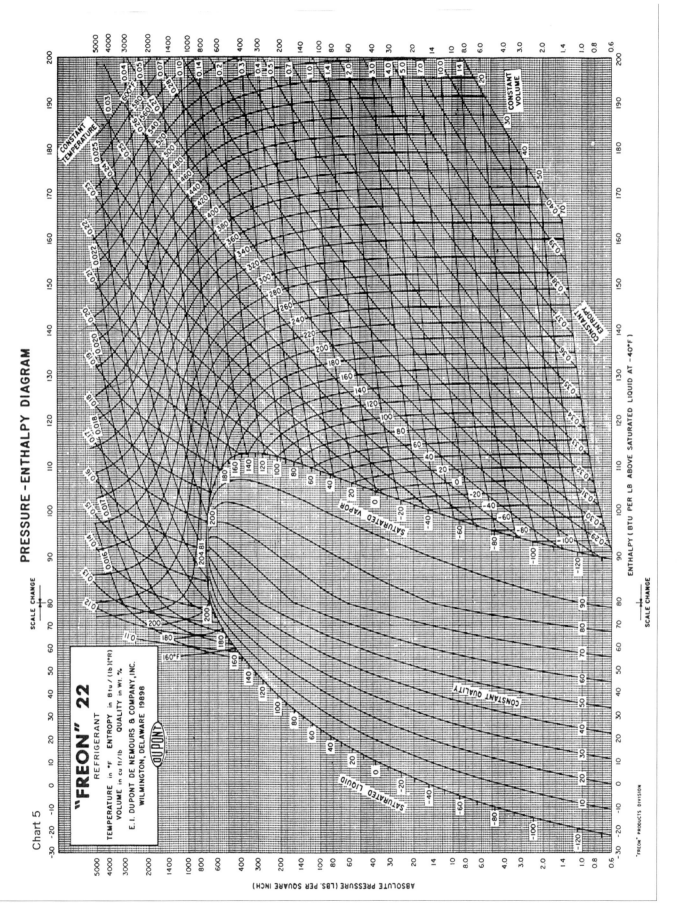

PRESSURE - ENTHALPY DIAGRAM

Chart 5

"FREON" 22
REFRIGERANT

TEMPERATURE in °F   ENTROPY in Btu / (lb.)(°R)
VOLUME in cu ft/lb   QUALITY in Wt.%
E. I. DUPONT DE NEMOURS & COMPANY, INC.
WILMINGTON, DELAWARE 1989B

DUPONT

ENTHALPY (BTU PER LB ABOVE SATURATED LIQUID AT -40°F)

ABSOLUTE PRESSURE (LBS. PER SQUARE INCH)

CONSTANT TEMPERATURE

CONSTANT VOLUME

CONSTANT ENTROPY

SATURATED VAPOR

CONSTANT QUALITY

SATURATED LIQUID

SCALE CHANGE

'FREON' PRODUCTS DIVISION

133

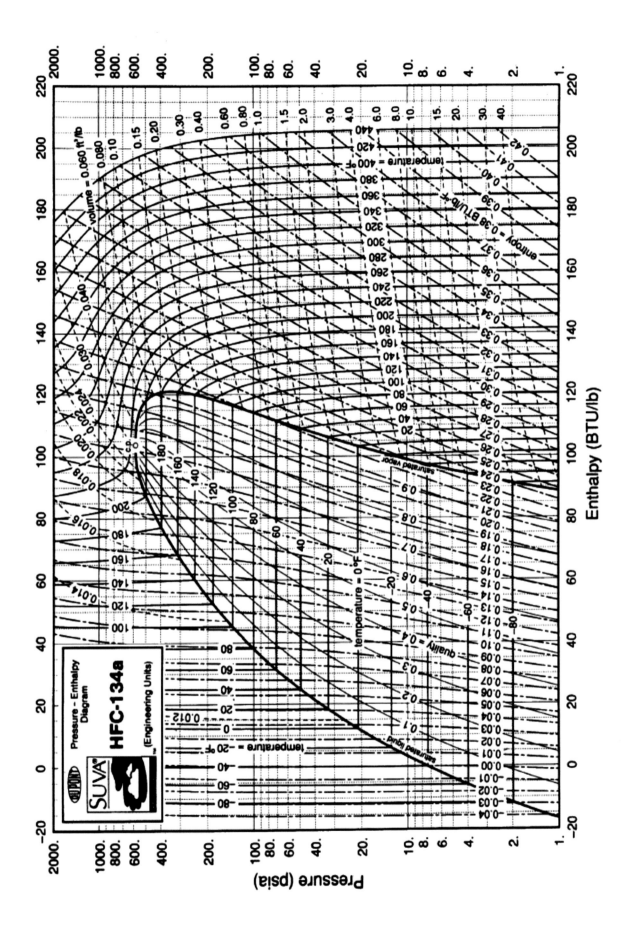

Pressure – Enthalpy Diagram
HFC-134a
(Engineering Units)

Enthalpy (BTU/lb)

Pressure (psia)

134

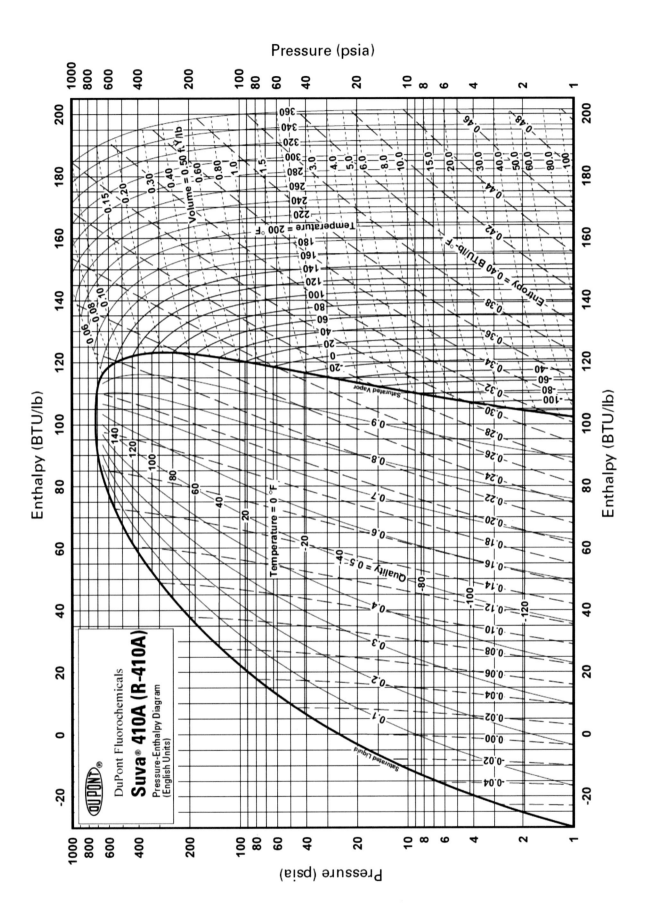

DuPont Fluorochemicals

Suva® 410A (R-410A)

Pressure-Enthalpy Diagram
(English Units)

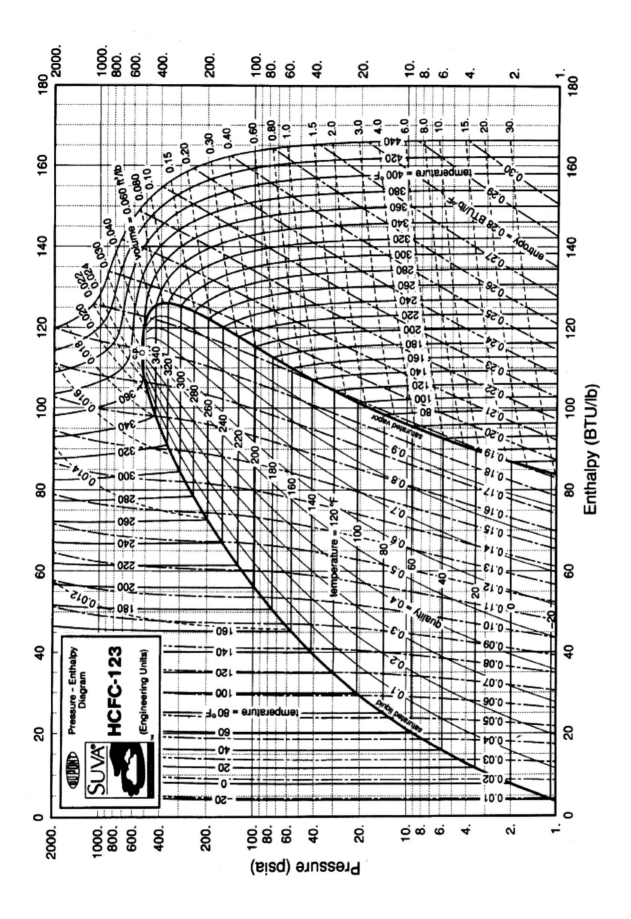

HCFC-123

Pressure – Enthalpy Diagram

(Engineering Units)

SUVA®

Enthalpy (BTU/lb)

Pressure (psia)

136

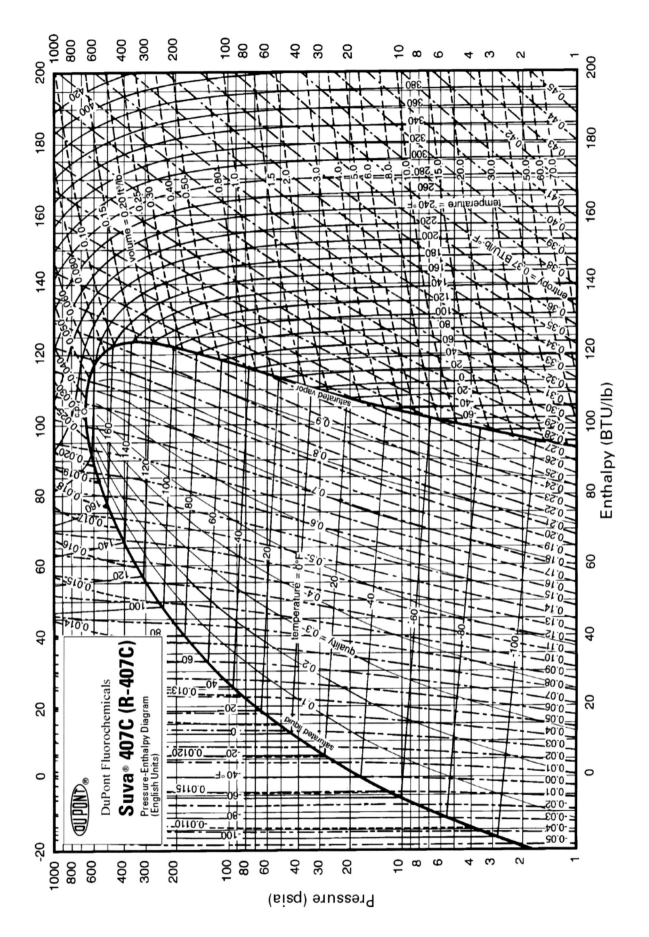

137

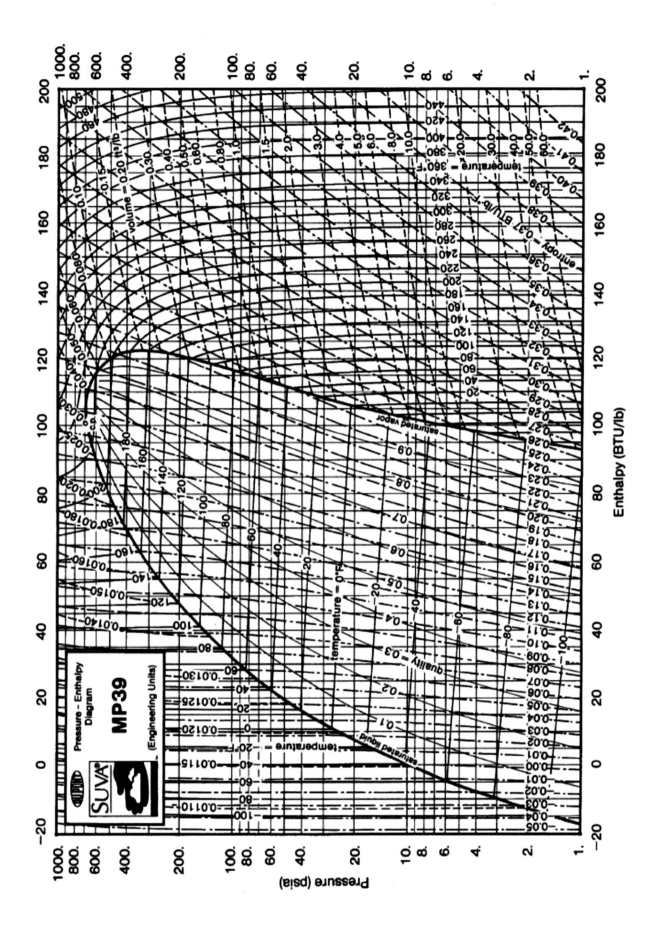

Pressure – Enthalpy Diagram

MP39

(Engineering Units)

SUVA®

Enthalpy (BTU/lb)

Pressure (psia)

TEST YOUR PRESSURE ENTHALPY KNOWLEDGE

01.　Explain why the MFR/ton increases as the NRE decreases.

02.　Explain why the THp/ton increases as the compression ratio increases.

03.　What happens to the EER as the compression ratio increases? Why?

04.　Reducing the amount of heat absorbed into the system through the suction line will affect the HOC. Will the HOC increase or decrease? Why?

05.　Reducing the amount of heat absorbed into the system through the suction line will affect the COP. Will the COP increase or decrease? Why?

06.　An air conditioning system is equipped with an automatic expansion valve. The condenser coil is blocked with dirt. What will happen to the system's compression ratio? What will happen to the system's HOW? What will happen to the system's mass flow rate? What will happen to the evaporator's capacity?

TEST YOUR PRESSURE ENTHALPY KNOWLEDGE
(Answers)

01. Explain why the MFR/ton increases as the NRE decreases.

The Net Refrigeration Effect provides the number of btus of heat energy that one pound of refrigerant can hold at the present operating conditions of the system. As the NRE drops the ability of the refrigerant to hold btus also drops. When such is the case, more refrigerant must be circulated through the system to obtain the same cooling result.

To provide one ton of cooling, 200 btus of heat energy must be transferred each minute. If one pound of refrigerant can absorb 200 btus of heat energy, only one pound of refrigerant must be circulated through the system each minute to obtain one ton of refrigeration. If the ability of the refrigerant to absorb heat decreases, the number of pounds of refrigerant that must be circulated through the system to obtain that same ton of refrigeration will increase.

So, as the NRE decreases the MFR/ton increases and vice versa.

02. Explain why the THp/ton increases as the compression ratio increases.

The THp/ton is calculated by the following formula:

$$THp/ton = (MFR/ton \times HOW) \div 42.42$$

As the compression ratio increases, the NRE decreases and the MFR/ton increases. See the answer to question #1 for more on this. In addition, when the compression ratio increases, the HOW increases as well. Since both factors in the numerator, MFR/ton and HOW, increase, the THp/ton will increase because the denominator of 42.42 remains the same.

In English, this means that, as the compression ratio increases, more work (and therefore horsepower) must be dedicated to increasing and decreasing the pressure of the refrigerant, so less power can be used to circulate refrigerant through the system. For this reason, more horsepower is required to obtain each ton of refrigeration.

03.   What happens to the EER as the compression ratio increases? Why?

As the compression ratio increases, the EER typically decreases. Here's how. As the compression ratio increases, the heat of work increases. An increase in the HOW results in an increase in the HOC and a decrease in the NRE. Since the COP of the system is equal to the NRE divided by the HOC, a decrease in the COP will result. Remember that the EER is equal to the COP times 3.413, so a decrease in COP will result in a decrease in EER.

04.   Reducing the amount of heat absorbed into the system through the suction line will affect the HOC. Will the HOC increase or decrease? Why?

Reducing the amount of heat absorbed into the system through the suction line will result in a decrease in HOC. The HOC is comprised of the heat of work, HOW and the suction line, so a decrease in the suction line heat will cause the HOC to drop, bringing it closer to the HOW.

05.   Reducing the amount of heat absorbed into the system through the suction line will affect the COP. Will the COP increase or decrease? Why?

From the answer to question #4, we can see that reducing the amount of heat absorbed into the system from the suction line will result in a reduced HOC. Reducing the HOC will result in an increase in the COP as long as the net refrigeration effect remained the same.

06.   An air conditioning system is equipped with an automatic expansion valve. The condenser coil is blocked with dirt. What will happen to the system's compression ratio? What will happen to the system's HOW? What will happen to the system's mass flow rate? What will happen to the evaporator's capacity?

The low side pressure of the system will remain the same, but the high side pressure will increase as a result of the dirty condense coil. An increase in the high side pressure will result in an increase in the compression ratio. An increase in compression ratio results in an increase in the heat of work. An increase in the heat of work causes a reduction in the MFR/system, which, in turn, causes a reduction in the capacity of the system's evaporator.

MORE COOL STUFF

The pages that follow provide some additional troubleshooting tools that can be used in conjunction with the pressure enthalpy information presented in this book. This additional information includes:

- Possible Causes for High Condenser Subcooling
- Possible Causes for Low Condenser Subcooling
- Possible Causes for Low Evaporator Superheat
- Possible Causes for High Evaporator Superheat
- Possible Causes for High Condenser Subcooling and Low Evaporator Superheat
- Possible Causes for Low Condenser Subcooling and High Evaporator Superheat
- Possible Causes for High Condenser Subcooling and High Evaporator Superheat

Heat Pump Stuff

- Possible Causes for High Head Pressure and Low Suction Pressure
  (System Operating in the Heating Mode. Cooling Mode Operating Correctly)
- Possible Causes for Low Head Pressure and High Suction Pressure
  (System Operating in the Heating Mode. Cooling Mode Operating Correctly)
- Possible Causes for Low Head Pressure and High Suction Pressure
  (System Operating in the Cooling Mode. Heating Mode Operating Correctly)
- Possible Causes for High Head Pressure and Low Suction Pressure
  (System Operating in the Cooling Mode. Heating Mode Operating Correctly)
- Possible Causes for Low Head Pressure and High Suction Pressure While Operating in Either Mode

Possible Causes for High Condenser Subcooling

✓ System overcharge
- o As the amount of refrigerant in the system increases, more refrigerant will back up into the condenser coil
- o As refrigerant backs up in the condenser, it spends more time in contact with the cooling medium allowing the refrigerant to reject more heat

✓ System operating in low-ambient conditions (air-cooled applications)
- o The temperature difference between the refrigerant and the air passing over the coil is greater, increasing the rate of heat transfer between the refrigerant and the condensing medium

✓ Refrigerant flow restriction in the liquid line
- o Liquid line restriction causes refrigerant to backup in the coil
- o As refrigerant backs up in the condenser, it spends more time in contact with the cooling medium allowing the refrigerant to reject more heat

✓ Clogged liquid line filter drier
- o Liquid line restriction causes refrigerant to backup in the coil
- o As refrigerant backs up in the condenser, it spends more time in contact with the cooling medium allowing the refrigerant to reject more heat

✓ Metering device stuck in the closed position
- o Liquid line restriction causes refrigerant to backup in the coil
- o As refrigerant backs up in the condenser, it spends more time in contact with the cooling medium allowing the refrigerant to reject more heat

✓ Overfeeding water-regulating valve (water-cooled applications)
- o The rate of heat transfer between the refrigerant and the water passing through the coil is greater because of the increased volume of water flowing through the condenser coil

✓ Noncondensable gases (air or nitrogen) in the system
- o Noncondensable gas takes up space in the condenser, reducing the effective heat transfer surface area
- o The temperature at the outlet of the condenser coil rises, but not as fast as the condenser saturation temperature

Possible Causes for Low Condenser Subcooling

✓ Dirty or blocked condenser coil (air-cooled applications)
   o Dirty or blocked condenser coils result in a reduction of condensing medium (air) flow through the coil
   o Refrigerant cannot reject heat quickly
   o Condensing process is slowed down
   o Vapor is present closer to the coil outlet
   o Results in high head pressure

✓ Reduced water flow through the condenser coil (water-cooled applications)
   o Reduced water flow reduced flow of condensing medium (water) through the coil
   o Rate of heat transfer from the refrigerant to the water is reduced
   o Condensing process is slowed down
   o Results in high head pressure

✓ Defective condenser fan motor (air-cooled applications)
   o Amount of airflow through the coil is greatly reduced
   o Refrigerant rejects heat slower
   o Effectiveness of the condenser is reduced
   o Results in high head pressure

✓ Loose or removed service panels on the condensing unit
   o Air bypasses the condenser coil
   o The amount of air passing through the coil is reduced
   o Less air passing through the coil leads to a reduction in the heat transfer rate from the refrigerant to the air passing through the coil
   o Results in high head pressure

✓ Defective water-regulating valve (water-cooled applications)
   o Reduced water flow through the valve results in less heat rejection by the refrigerant
   o Results in high head pressure

✓ Scale buildup in the tubes of the water-cooled condenser
   o Scale acts as an insulator and prevents the refrigerant from rejecting heat to the water
   o Indicated by high head pressure and a low delta-t across the water side of the condenser
   o Results in high head pressure

Possible Causes for Low Evaporator Superheat

✓ Refrigerant overcharge (except systems with thermostatic expansion valves)
- o Refrigerant will take a longer period of time to completely vaporize
- o Liquid will be present closer to the outlet of the coil
- o Results in a higher suction pressure

✓ Overfeeding metering device
- o Refrigerant will take a longer period of time to completely vaporize
- o Liquid will be present closer to the outlet of the coil
- o Results in a higher suction pressure

✓ Improper superheat spring adjustment on TXV system (spring pressure too low)
- o Too much refrigerant being fed into the evaporator coil
- o Refrigerant will take a longer period of time to completely vaporize
- o Liquid will be present closer to the outlet of the coil
- o Results in a higher suction pressure

✓ Improperly mounted thermostatic expansion valve thermal bulb (loose bulb)
- o The air surrounding the suction line at the outlet of the evaporator coil is warmer than the suction line itself
- o The bulb will therefore be warmer
- o The TXV will open to feed more refrigerant into the coil in an attempt to lower the superheat
- o Too much refrigerant being fed into the evaporator coil
- o Refrigerant will take a longer period of time to completely vaporize
- o Liquid will be present closer to the outlet of the coil
- o Results in a higher suction pressure

✓ Blocked or dirty evaporator coil
- o Reduced airflow through the coil
- o Refrigerant absorbs less heat due to reduced airflow
- o Less heat results is a lower saturation temperature and pressure
- o Refrigerant takes longer to boil off into a vapor

✓ Dirty or clogged air filter
- o Reduced airflow through the coil
- o Refrigerant absorbs less heat due to reduced airflow
- o Less heat results is a lower saturation temperature and pressure
- o Refrigerant takes longer to boil off into a vapor

✓ Defective evaporator fan motor
- o Reduced airflow through the coil
- o Refrigerant absorbs less heat due to reduced airflow
- o Less heat results is a lower saturation temperature and pressure
- o Refrigerant takes longer to boil off into a vapor

✓ Broken or loose belt (belt-driven blower assembly applications)
- o Blower will not turn (broken belt) or will turn at reduced speed (loose belt)
- o Reduced airflow through the coil
- o Refrigerant absorbs less heat due to reduced airflow
- o Less heat results is a lower saturation temperature and pressure
- o Refrigerant takes longer to boil off into a vapor

✓ Reduced water flow through chiller barrel (chilled water applications)
- o Less water flow results in less heat available to be absorbed by the refrigerant
- o Refrigerant absorbs less heat due to reduced water flow
- o Less heat results is a lower saturation temperature and pressure
- o Refrigerant takes longer to boil off into a vapor in the chiller barrel

✓ Noncondensable gases in the system (capillary tube systems)
- o Capillary tubes have a fixed pressure drop
- o Evaporator saturation pressure will be higher
- o Rate of heat being absorbed will be lower
- o Less heat being absorbed leads to slower vaporization

Possible Causes for High Evaporator Superheat

✓ Refrigerant undercharge
  - A reduction in system refrigerant charge allows refrigerant to vaporize quickly in the coil
  - The last drop of liquid is closer to the inlet of the coil
  - More of the coil is used for a sensible heat transfer
  - The temperature of the refrigerant is higher at the outlet of the coil

✓ Improper superheat spring adjustment on the thermostatic expansion valve (too high)
  - Superheat spring is causing the valve to be pushed closed
  - Evaporator coil is underfed
  - Reduced amount of refrigerant in the evaporator coil boils quickly
  - The last drop of liquid is closer to the inlet of the coil
  - More of the coil is used for a sensible heat transfer
  - The temperature of the refrigerant is therefore higher at the outlet of the coil

✓ Blocked or clogged inlet strainer on the thermostatic expansion valve
  - Blockage results in reduced refrigerant flow into the evaporator coil
  - Evaporator coil is underfed
  - Reduced amount of refrigerant in the evaporator coil boils quickly
  - The last drop of liquid is closer to the inlet of the coil
  - More of the coil is used for a sensible heat transfer
  - The temperature of the refrigerant is therefore higher at the outlet of the coil

✓ Blocked or clogged capillary tube
  - Blockage results in reduced refrigerant flow into the evaporator coil
  - Evaporator coil is underfed
  - Reduced amount of refrigerant in the evaporator coil boils quickly
  - The last drop of liquid is closer to the inlet of the coil
  - More of the coil is used for a sensible heat transfer
  - The temperature of the refrigerant is therefore higher at the outlet of the coil

✓ Underfeeding metering device
  - Evaporator coil is underfed
  - Reduced amount of refrigerant in the evaporator coil boils quickly
  - The last drop of liquid is closer to the inlet of the coil
  - More of the coil is used for a sensible heat transfer
  - The temperature of the refrigerant is therefore higher at the outlet of the coil

Possible Causes for High Condenser Subcooling and Low Evaporator Superheat

✓ System overcharge
- o High condenser subcooling is an indication that the system is overcharged
- o Refrigerant is backing up in the condenser coil
- o Low evaporator superheat is an indication that the system is overcharged
- o The evaporator is being overfed
- o Therefore, there is too much refrigerant in both the evaporator and the condenser coil

Side note:

This situation is more prevalent on capillary tube systems since they are critically charged systems. Critically charged systems are those that are not equipped with refrigerant receivers and all of the refrigerant is flowing through the system at all times. Refrigerant receivers are system devices that are intended to accept excess system refrigerant and are commonly found on systems that modulate refrigerant flow, such as those equipped with automatic expansion valves, AXVs, or thermostatic expansion valves, TXVs.

On systems that are equipped with TXVs, the condenser subcooling will be high, but the evaporator superheat will be normal. The sole purpose of the TXV is to maintain a constant evaporator superheat, so the valve will close to maintain the evaporator superheat at the desired level.

Possible Causes for Low Condenser Subcooling and High Evaporator Superheat

✓ System undercharge
- o Low condenser subcooling is an indication that the system is undercharged
- o Low evaporator superheat is an indication that the system is undercharged
- o The evaporator is underfed
- o Therefore, there is too little refrigerant in both the evaporator and the condenser coil

Possible Causes for High Condenser Subcooling and High Evaporator Superheat

- ✓ Improper superheat spring adjustment on the thermostatic expansion valve (too high)
  - ○ Superheat spring is causing the valve to be pushed closed
  - ○ Evaporator coil is underfed
  - ○ Reduced amount of refrigerant in the evaporator coil boils quickly
  - ○ The last drop of liquid is closer to the inlet of the coil
  - ○ More of the coil is used for a sensible heat transfer
  - ○ The temperature of the refrigerant is higher at the outlet of the coil
  - ○ Refrigerant backs up on the high side of the system

- ✓ Blocked or clogged inlet strainer on the thermostatic expansion valve
  - ○ Superheat spring is causing the valve to be pushed closed
  - ○ Evaporator coil is underfed
  - ○ Reduced amount of refrigerant in the evaporator coil boils quickly
  - ○ The last drop of liquid is closer to the inlet of the coil
  - ○ More of the coil is used for a sensible heat transfer
  - ○ The temperature of the refrigerant is higher at the outlet of the coil
  - ○ Refrigerant backs up on the high side of the system

- ✓ Blocked or clogged capillary tube
  - ○ Evaporator coil is underfed
  - ○ Reduced amount of refrigerant in the evaporator coil boils quickly
  - ○ The last drop of liquid is closer to the inlet of the coil
  - ○ More of the coil is used for a sensible heat transfer
  - ○ The temperature of the refrigerant is higher at the outlet of the coil
  - ○ Refrigerant backs up on the high side of the system

- ✓ Underfeeding metering device
  - ○ Evaporator coil is underfed
  - ○ Reduced amount of refrigerant in the evaporator coil boils quickly
  - ○ The last drop of liquid is closer to the inlet of the coil
  - ○ More of the coil is used for a sensible heat transfer
  - ○ The temperature of the refrigerant is higher at the outlet of the coil
  - ○ Refrigerant backs up on the high side of the system

Side note:

High subcooling is an indication of excessive refrigerant charge, while high superheat is an indication of an undercharge. Since it appears that there is an imbalance in the system (too much refrigerant on the high side and not enough on the low side), the likely causes for this situation all involve the metering device, which facilitates refrigerant flow from the high side of the system to the low side.

Heat Pump Stuff

Possible Causes for High Head Pressure and Low Suction Pressure
(System Operating in the Heating Mode. Cooling Mode Operating Correctly)

✓ Indoor check valve stuck in the closed position
✓ Outdoor metering device stuck in the closed position
✓ Outdoor filter drier clogged

Possible Causes for Low Head Pressure and High Suction Pressure
(System Operating in the Heating Mode. Cooling Mode Operating Correctly)

✓ Outdoor check valve stuck in the open position
✓ Indoor metering device stuck in the open position

Possible Causes for Low Head Pressure and High Suction Pressure
(System Operating in the Cooling Mode. Heating Mode Operating Correctly)

✓ Indoor check valve stuck in the open position
✓ Indoor metering device stuck in the open position

Possible Causes for High Head Pressure and Low Suction Pressure
(System Operating in the Cooling Mode. Heating Mode Operating Correctly)

✓ Outdoor check valve stuck in the closed position
✓ Indoor metering device stuck in the closed position
✓ Indoor filter drier clogged

Possible Causes for Low Head Pressure and High Suction Pressure
While Operating in Either Mode (Both modes malfunctioning)

✓ Internal reversing valve leak
✓ Damaged compressor valves

NOTES

NOTES

NOTES

NOTES